World History Journey Across Time

Unit 4 Resources

The Middle Ages

New York, New York Columbus, Ohio Chicago, Illinois Peoria, Illinois Woodland Hills, California

Book Organization

Glencoe offers resources that accompany *Journey Across Time* to expand, enrich, review, and assess every lesson you teach and for every student you teach. Now Glencoe has organized its many resources for the way you teach.

How This Book Is Organized

Each Unit Resources book is divided into three parts—unit-based resources, chapter-based resources, and section-based resources. Glencoe has included tabs at the side of every activity page in this book to help you navigate.

Unit-Based Resources

We have organized this book so that all unit resources appear at the beginning. Although you may choose to use the specific activities at any time during the course of unit study, Glencoe has placed these resources up front so that you can review your options.

Chapter-Based and Section-Based Resources

Chapter-based resources follow the unit materials. These activities are directly tied to their chapter and should be used during the course of chapter study. A description of each of the many chapter activities available to you in this book can be found on page v. Following the chapter-based resources are the Vocabulary and Guided Reading Activities—one per each section of the Student Edition.

A Complete Answer Key

A complete answer key appears at the back of this book. This answer key includes answers for all activities in this book in the order in which the activities appear.

Photo Credits: Page 13: Archives Charmet/Bridgeman Art Library; Page 45: Ramon Manent/CORBIS; Page 73: Ancient Art & Architecture Collection; Page 101: Bildarchiv Steffens/Bridgeman Art Library

The McGraw·Hill Companies

Send all inquiries to:
Glencoe/McGraw-Hill
8787 Orion Place
Columbus, Ohio 43240-4027

ISBN 0-07-869470-1

Printed in the United States of America.

1 2 3 4 5 6 7 8 9 079 10 09 08 07 06 05

Table of Contents

Table of Contents

Chapter 14: Medieval Japan

Chapter 15: Medieval Europe

To the Teacher

Journey Across Time Unit Resources

Glencoe's Unit Resources books are packed with activities for the varied needs of all of your students. They include the following activities:

Unit-Based Activities

- **Step Into World History Activities**

These activities are designed to give students an idea about real life occurrences in history that they can feel a part of—to make history come alive! Through research, cooperative activities, simulations, and teaching strategies, these activities allow you to give students a taste of historical events first hand. There is also a pacing guide to help you plan your class time.

Chapter-Based Activities

- **Activities for Differentiated Instruction**

The *Journey Across Time* Activities for Differentiated Instruction provide students with a cross-curricular connection between history and other subjects. These activities also give you an opportunity to differentiate your instruction, addressing the different types of learners in your classroom.

- **Critical Thinking Skills Activities**

Critical thinking skills are important to students because they provide the tools to live and work in an ever-changing world. These activities show students how to use information to make judgments, develop their own ideas, and apply what they have learned to new situations.

- **Geography and History Activities**

These interdisciplinary activities provide students with the opportunity to analyze and interpret maps in relation to historical events. Students practice using geography skills as an aid to understanding history.

- **People to Meet Activities**

The activities focus on interesting and important figures in history who have had a lasting impact on future generations. Students will read about famous, and not so well known people from throughout history.

- **Time Line Activities**

The *Journey Across Time* Time Line Activities use time lines of different periods of history to help students become aware of chronology and to locate major historical events in time. Comparative time lines allow students to see relationships among events in different regions of the country, among events in different countries, or among events on different continents.

- **Citizenship and Service Learning Activities**

These application activities give students the opportunity to participate in grassroots community projects that may have national or international implications.

- **Economic Activities**

These interdisciplinary activities analyze and interpret historical concepts in relation to economics and the economies of the world's regions. The activities are designed to help students appreciate how economics and history are interrelated.

- **World Literature Readings**

These readings provide literature by or about people who live in each of the world's geographic regions. Each selection is preceded by background information and a guided reading suggestion, and followed by comprehension and critical thinking questions.

- **Primary Source Readings**

The *Journey Across Time* Primary Source Readings allow students to see history through the eyes of those who witnessed historic events, lived in historic periods, and participated in historic cultures. The skills involved with interpreting primary sources are a part of the student activities in this booklet.

- **Take-Home Review Activities**

These activities contain information and activities that students and their families/caregivers can do at home to reinforce an understanding of chapter content. They are intended to give parents easy (not challenging) materials to help their children with chapter lessons.

Section-Based Activities

- **Vocabulary Activities**

These review and reinforcement activities help students to master unfamiliar terms used in the student textbook. The worksheets emphasize identification of word meanings and are intended to build student vocabularies.

- **Guided Reading Activities**

These activities provide help for students who are having difficulty comprehending the student textbook. Students fill in missing information in the guided reading outlines, sentence completion activities, or other information-organizing exercises as they read the textbook.

Unit 4 Resources

The Middle Ages

Census of the School

Topic

In this simulation, students will take a census of the school. They will decide what information to obtain, analyze data, and draw conclusions.

Purpose

Two of the civilizations discussed in this unit—Nara Japan and England under William the Conqueror—conducted censuses to determine the wealth and resources of the respective lands. A census is an official count of the population. The U.S. Constitution requires a census in the United States every 10 years to decide congressional representation. The students will be recreating the census process.

Objectives

By participating in this simulation, students will:

- Learn how a census is conducted and review the history of census taking in medieval Europe.
- Conduct a census of their school, determining the data to be collected and how to collect it.
- Analyze the data collected and draw conclusions from it.
- Practice public speaking and participation in an interactive group.

Suggested Resources

- Library and Internet resources related to taking a census
- Copies of the census form from 2000 are available from the Integrated Public Use Microdata Series at the University of Minnesota, www.ipum.umn.edu/usa/voliii/tEnumForm.html

Procedures/Pacing Guide

This simulation is designed to be conducted over six days.

Day One—Introduce the Simulation

Review the two censuses mentioned in Chapters 14 and 15. Make sure that students understand the purpose behind each. Ask if students know that the U.S. Constitution requires that a census be taken every 10 years. Explain that the results of the census determine each state's number of representatives in the U.S. Congress. Next, ask students how they would go about conducting a census at their school. Inform them that over the next few days they will be conducting a census. Present the idea that a census is like a snapshot in time because population data changes rapidly. As homework, assign Simulation Sheet 1. It takes students through a census of their own belongings.

Day Two—Planning and Research

Go over Simulation Sheet 1 and focus on how the students collected data, not on the results of the count. Be sensitive to the fact that some children have fewer belongings than others. Form the class into small groups. Over the course of 20 minutes, have the groups select five pieces of data they would like to collect about their school. When the time is up, have each group report. Record their responses on the board, eliminating duplicates. Lead the class in narrowing down the data categories to five, such as number of people in the school, gender, number of computers, and ways to get to school (bus, subway, car, walk).

As homework, ask each student to spend some time in the classroom, media center, or at home reviewing the following Web sites: www.census.gov, the site of the U.S. census; www.genealogy.com, for information on past censuses; and www.ipums.umn.edu/usa, a University

Census of the School (continued)

of Minnesota site. They should answer the questions on Simulation Sheet 2.

Day Three—Prepare to Collect Data

Make sure on this day that you inform the principal and other teachers and staff that your students will be taking a census on Day Four. Help students determine their locations for data collection. Make sure students collect data in each classroom of the school as well as the library, office, and other rooms. Have students prepare a form to collect the data. Duplicate the form.

Assign students to collect data in pairs. Each pair should be given specific locations in which to collect, making sure that all locations in the school are covered. Discuss and rehearse proper etiquette for entering a room, announcing your purpose, and taking the count. Make sure the students thank people for participating.

Day Four—Conduct the Census

After meeting in class for a brief review of their tasks, pairs of students go to their assigned locations to collect their data. Gather the data sheets, which will be analyzed the next day.

Day Five—Analyze Data

On the board, write the five categories of data. Have students read their results as other students record them on the board. Have several students use calculators to add the results. Start with raw totals. Find the number of people in the school, students, staff, males, females, and so on. Then, have pairs of students work on particular problems, like the average number of students per classroom, average number of computers per classroom, and so on. Have them make a bar graph of their results. Assist students in writing a group report of their results.

Day Six—Reflect

Ask students to discuss how the census went. Did they have any noteworthy experiences? What would they change if they did this again? What surprised them? Invite the principal to your room to receive a copy of the report.

Name______________________________ Date_______________________ Class_______________________

STEP INTO WORLD HISTORY ACTIVITY 4

Sock Census

Simulation Sheet 1

UNIT 4

Directions: Answer the questions in the spaces given. This worksheet will introduce you to taking a census—a count of things. In this case, you will be counting socks found in your home.

1. How many socks are in your home?

____

2. How did you count the socks? (Did you touch each pair? Did you ask other people to tell you how many they had?)

____

3. Where are socks located that might have been missed in the count? (Did you check the dirty and clean laundry? Did you count the socks that were on people's feet?)

____

____

4. How did you keep track of the number of socks as you counted? (Did you count them in your head? Did you make marks on a tablet?)

____

5. How would you keep track of the colors of the socks as well as the number of socks in your home?

____

____

6. In the space below, make a data table you could use when counting the socks in your home and recording their colors.

Name ______________________ Date ______________________ Class ______________________

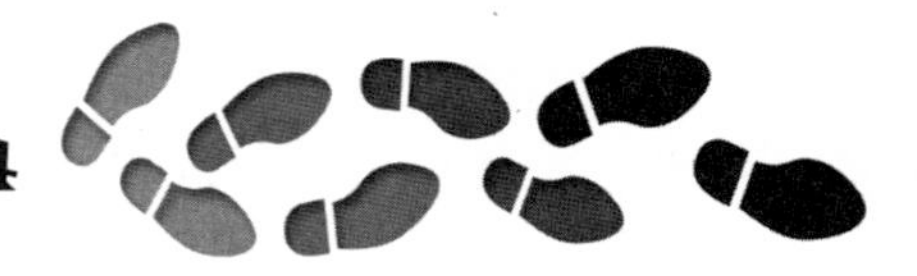

Census of the School

Simulation Sheet 2

Directions: Answer the following questions in the spaces provided. Use a computer at your local library or one from your school to go to this Web site of the U.S. Census Bureau: www.census.gov.

1. How would you find information about your own state? What information is available about your state?

____

____

2. Click on "Maps" from the "Geography" menu. Then click on "What's New." Find the county map for your state. What color is the map? What program opened it? Print out the map, color in your own county with a marker, and staple it to this sheet.

____

3. What would you click to find housing statistics?

____

4. Click on "Your Gateway to Census 2000." Then click on "street address." Enter the street address for your home or school. How many different geographic divisions is your address a part of? Name five of them.

____

____

____

5. Highlight one of the subdivisions and then click "Map It." What color is the map? Can you locate where your home or school would be? Print out this map, placing an "X" where your home or school is located. Staple the map to this sheet.

____

6. Why do you think so much of the census information is available free of charge?

____

____

____

Chapter 12 Resources

China in the Middle Ages

Name________________________ Date__________________ Class__________________

Activity for Differentiated Instruction 12

Sui and Tang Dynasties

The Sui and Tang dynasties reunited and rebuilt China after years of war. Though the Sui dynasty was rather short-lived, the Tang dynasty was in power for about 300 years (A.D. 618–907). The map below illustrates the expansion of—and subsequent attacks against—China during the Tang dynasty.

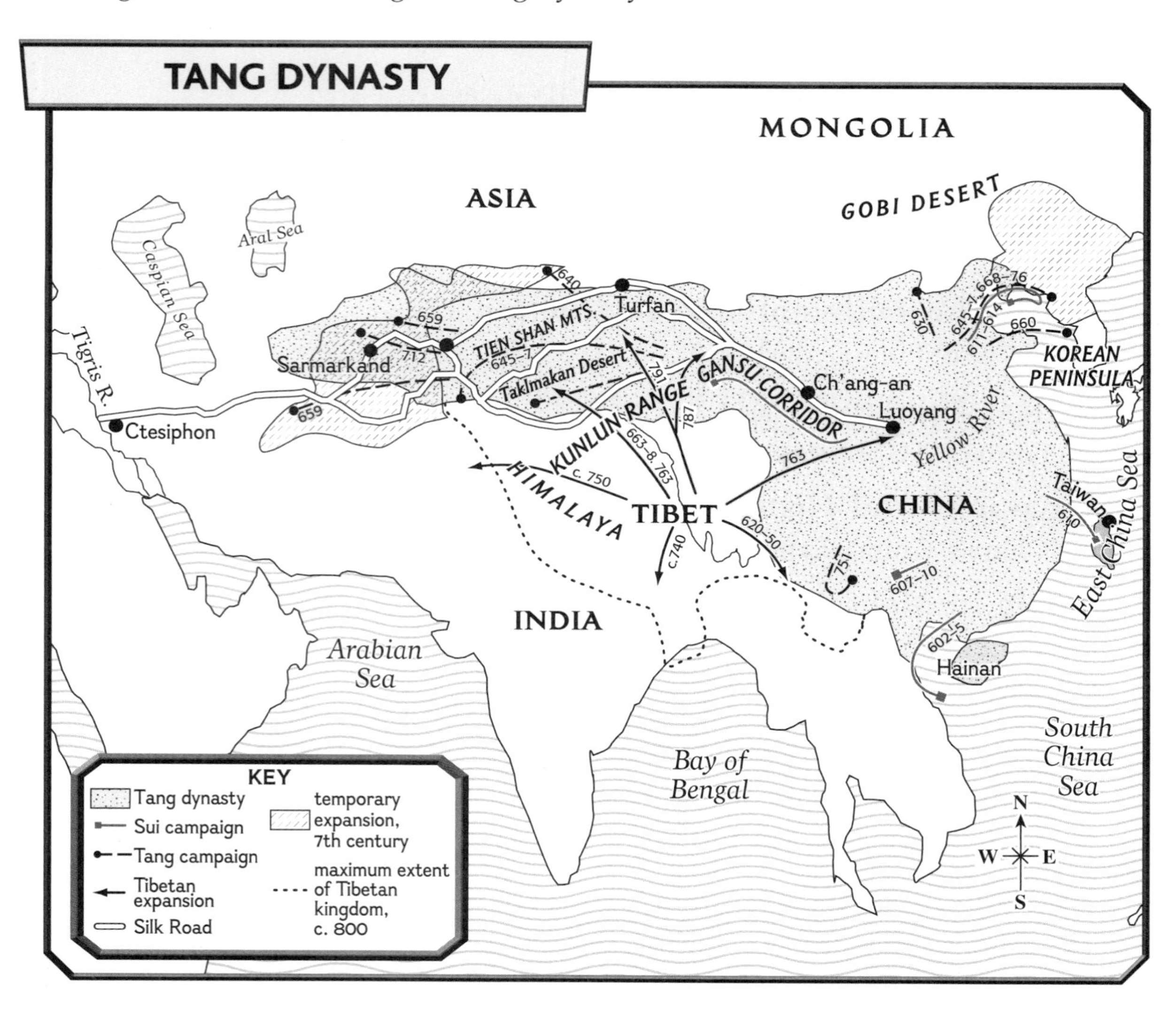

Directions: Use the information in the map and your textbook to answer the following questions on a separate sheet of paper.

1. **Geography Skills** Which two bodies of water formed the eastern border of China during the Tang dynasty?

2. **Cause and Effect** What do you think was the economic impact of the loss of the Gansu Corridor to the Tang dynasty? Explain your answer.

Teaching Strategies for Different Learning Styles

The following are ways that the basic lesson can be modified to accommodate students' different learning styles.

Verbal/Linguistic Learning; Intrapersonal Learning

Have students research the events at the River Talas in A.D. 751 and their impact on the Tang dynasty. Ask them to present their findings in a two-page paper.

Kinesthetic Learning; Interpersonal Learning

Divide the class into three groups. Assign one group the Sui dynasty, one the Tang dynasty, and one the Five Dynasties or Civil War period. Students in each group should use the library or Internet to research the size and geography of their dynasty. Then they should construct relief maps of China during their dynasty, using clay and/or other materials of their choice.

Logical/Mathematical Learning; Visual/Spatial Learning

Assign students the following questions: (1) Consult a modern map of China. At its greatest extent, how large was Tang dynasty China compared with modern-day China? (2) Find the distance between the following: Changan and Luoyang; Hangzhou and Guangzhou. (3) How many years elapsed between the first Sui campaign into Korea and the first Tang campaign?

Auditory/Musical Learning

Distribute to students several poems of the Tang dynasty. Ask students to write a melody to go with the words.

Visual/Spatial Learning

Have students construct a table to chart the military campaigns of the Sui and Tang dynasties. Have them include dates of campaigns and their general geographic movement. Consult a modern map, if necessary, to help with descriptions.

Gifted and Talented

The Tang dynasty is often called a "golden age" for Chinese art and literature. Ask students to speculate on the reasons art and literature flourished during this time. They should present their ideas, with ample corroboration, in a two- to three-page report.

CRISS Reading Strategy

RAFT (**R**ole, **A**udience, **F**ormat, **T**opic) is a writing tool that directs students to look at a topic from a different perspective. Tell students that emperor Taizong needs to recruit more soldiers to expand the empire into central Asia and help take final control of the Silk Road. Have students take on the **R**ole of a military recruiter addressing a specific **A**udience—Chinese men. Students should choose the **F**ormat of a short speech given in the town square and write five reasons on the **T**opic of why the men should enlist in the army to serve the emperor.

English Learners (EL) Reading Strategy

Have EL students write the names of all the cities and rivers shown on the map. Also ask them to identify the names of all of the bodies of water shown on the map. Finally, have them explain the significance of the arrows shown on the map.

Name______________________________ Date____________________ Class____________________

Critical Thinking Skills Activity 12

Forming Hypotheses

Social Studies Objective: Analyze information and form hypotheses.

Learning the Skill

A **hypothesis** is a theory or possible explanation of events based on evidence. After gathering evidence about an event, you can form hypotheses about why things happened.

- Ask questions—such as *why, how, where, when, which,* and *if*—about something that has happened.
- Form a hypothesis for why it happened.
- Gather and analyze information to prove or disprove your hypothesis.

Practicing the Skill

Directions: Read the following paragraphs about the ancient city of Loulan on the Silk Road. Then answer the questions that follow.

Loulan was founded in the A.D. 100s beside Lop Nur Lake and had flourished as a trading center. After 800 years, the city suddenly vanished from recorded history.

At its height, Loulan had been home to 14,000 people. It was an important trading center on the Silk Road, connecting China and the West. The oasis at Loulan offered travelers a comfortable stop on their long journey.

At the beginning of the 1900s, a Swedish explorer discovered the ruins of Loulan in the sand on the shore of a lake that had dried up long ago.

In 1980, the body of a striking woman, perfectly preserved by the dry desert sands, was uncovered. The "Loulan Beauty" as she came to be called, had died almost 3,800 years ago. Tall and slender, wrapped in brightly colored silk clothing covered with Celtic designs, she had blonde hair and Caucasian features. As other mummies were uncovered, archaeologists found an entire settlement of Caucasian Western Europeans in the middle of northwest China.

1. What possible reasons could have caused the city to vanish from recorded history?

____

____

____

2. What might explain the presence of Caucasian Western Europeans in Loulan?

____

____

____

CHAPTER 12

Name ______________________ Date ________________ Class ________________

Geography and History Activity 12

China's Grand Canal

The eastern section of China is a relatively flat region with several long rivers. The rivers flow from west to east across much of China, emptying into the East China and Yellow Seas, which are parts of the Pacific Ocean. In that part of the country, no rivers flow in a north-south direction. Because so many goods in China were moved by water, trade within the country was hurt.

In 486 B.C., building began on a canal running from north to south. It took nine years to complete the first section between the city of Suzhou and the Chang Jiang. It was 53 miles (85 km) long. Over the next few centuries the canal was extended in both directions and became known as the Grand Canal. More cities and rivers were connected. By the time it was completed in the A.D. 600s, the Grand Canal was between 1,100 and 1,200 miles (1,770 and 1,931 km) long.

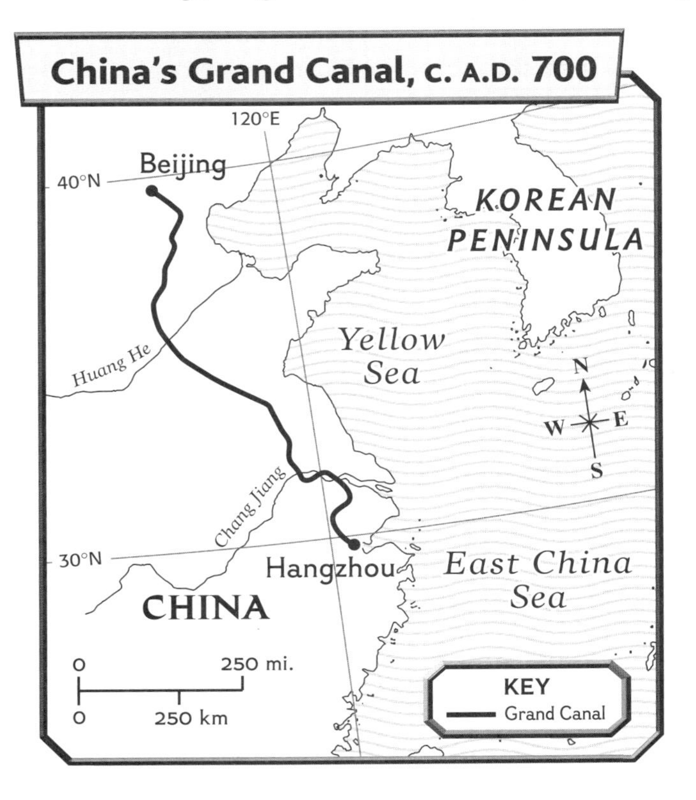

Thousands of Lives for Every Mile

The major phase of construction took place during a six-year period between A.D. 605 and 611. Sections of the canal between Beijing in the north and Hangzhou in the south were connected and widened. At some points the canal was 100 feet (31 m) wide. About 60 stone bridges were built across it.

An estimated three million people who worked on the canal died from hard labor and starvation. Many people thought the canal was a waste of money and human lives. The dynasty that ordered the construction of the greatest part of the canal was overthrown in A.D. 618.

Name________________________ Date__________________ Class____________________

China's Grand Canal

The Grand Canal was one of the greatest construction projects of ancient times. It was and still is the longest human-made waterway in the world. When finished, it connected five rivers and numerous cities. Wheat and manufactured goods from the north were exchanged for rice and textiles from the south. Thanks to the canal, China enjoyed great prosperity for many years.

Comparing the Grand Canal and Other Canals

Name of Canal and Location	Bodies of Water Connected	Length and Number of Locks	Year(s) Opened
Grand Canal China	Huang He, Haihe, Chang Jiang, Qian-tang, and Huaihe rivers	1,114 mi. (1,792 km) 24 locks	495 B.C.– A.D. 611
Erie Canal United States	Hudson River and Great Lakes	363 mi. (584 km) 77 locks	1825
Panama Canal Panama	Caribbean Sea and Pacific Ocean	51 mi. (82 km) 3 locks	1914
Suez Canal Egypt	Red Sea and Mediterranean Sea	100 mi. (161 km) 0 locks	1869

Directions: Answer the following questions in the spaces provided.

1. Why was a canal necessary in early China? ____________________

____

2. How long was the Grand Canal upon its completion in the A.D. 600s?

____

3. Which two cities were on the north and south ends of the Grand Canal?

____

4. Why was the dynasty that completed the Grand Canal overthrown?

____

____

5. **Compare and Contrast** In the chart, what is the second-longest canal listed? About how many times longer was the Grand Canal than that canal?

____

____

Name______________________________ Date______________________ Class______________________

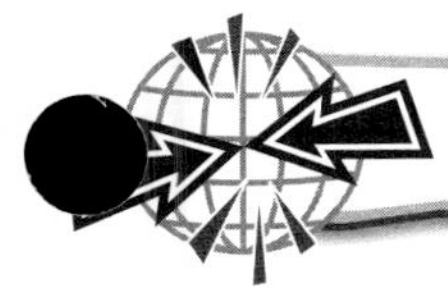

People to Meet Activity 12

Wu Zetian

Wu was born in China during the Tang dynasty in A.D. 625. She and other rich noblewomen had more freedom than women did in earlier and later dynasties. Wu learned to play music and to read and write. At 13 she joined the imperial court. Soon she became admired for her intelligence and beauty.

Gaining and Keeping Power

Wu married Kao Tsung a few years after he became emperor. When Kao became paralyzed by a stroke, Wu took over the government.

She protected her power as ruthlessly as any man of that time. She created a secret police force and killed many enemies, including three of her own children. When Kao died, Wu made her youngest son the emperor because he obeyed her orders.

In A.D. 690, Wu's son stepped down, and Wu became empress. People did not like women ruling directly. To help people accept her rule, Wu hired scholars to write about famous women. She also gave her mother's relatives powerful positions in government.

Empress Wu

During her rule Wu invited scholars to China, built temples, and encouraged artists. She made the army smaller and made Buddhism the state religion. She also helped the peasants by increasing agricultural production and building public works like irrigation canals.

In A.D. 705, Wu's third son pushed her out of power. And Wu, the only empress in China's history, died that same year.

Directions: Answer the questions below in the spaces provided.

1. List four things—good or bad—that Empress Wu did.

____

2. Why did Wu want to change how people felt about women rulers?

____

3. **Writing** On another sheet of paper, write an obituary of Empress Wu's life. You may need to look at other obituaries in the newspaper to see how they are done.

Name______________________ Date______________________ Class______________________

Time Line Activity 12

Kublai Khan and Marco Polo (A.D. 1216–1296)

Directions: Use the background information to create a time line about Kublai Khan and Marco Polo.

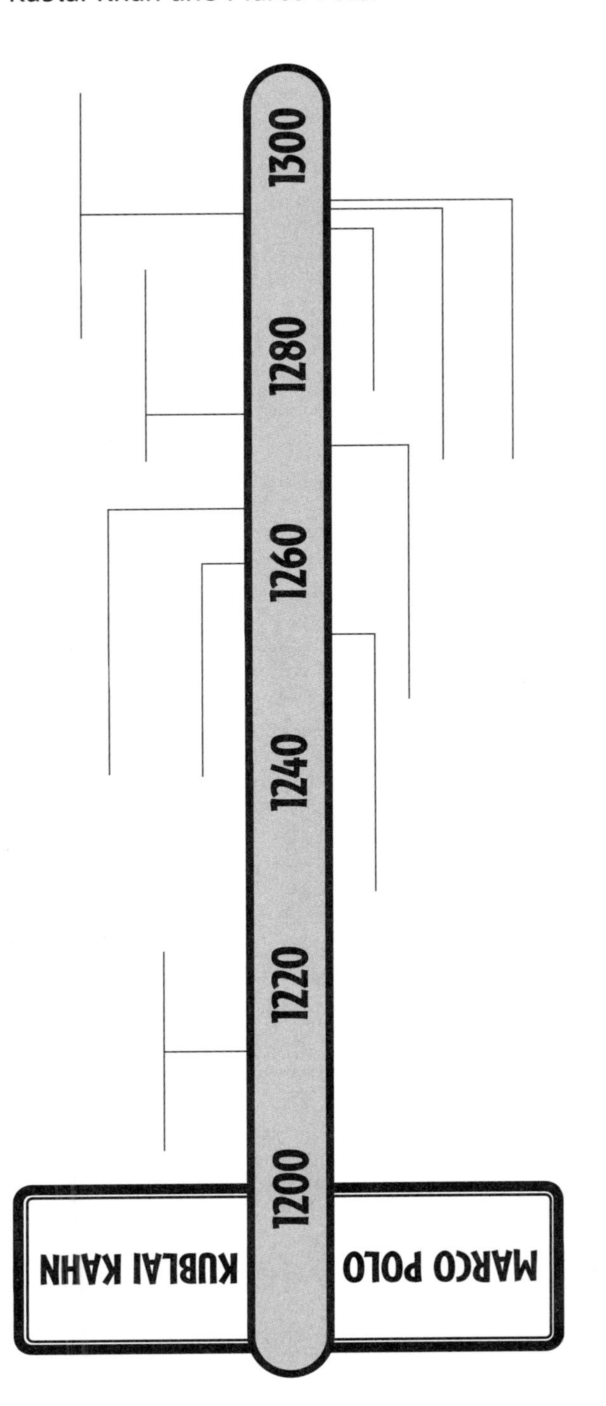

Background
Marco Polo traveled to China with his father and uncle in the late 1200s. Kublai Khan was fascinated by Marco Polo's stories about his travels. He sent Marco Polo on many fact-finding trips. After Marco Polo returned to Venice, he wrote a book about his travels. This book, called *Description of the World*, amazed Europeans with its accounts of the wonders of China.

KUBLAI KHAN

- Kublai was born in 1215.
- He became the new khan in 1260.
- Four years later, he moved his capital to Khanbaliq (now Beijing).
- In 1276 Kublai Khan's army took Quinsay.
- He died in 1294.

MARCO POLO

- Marco Polo was born in Venice in 1254.
- When he was 17, he left for China.
- In 1292 the Polos left China.
- They arrived back in Venice three years later.
- The next year, Marco Polo was captured in battle and put in prison.

Name______________________________ Date____________________ Class__________________

CITIZENSHIP AND SERVICE LEARNING ACTIVITY 12

Civil Service Jobs Poster

Why It's Important

Many employees of the United States government are hired using a process developed in ancient China—the civil service system. Civil service employees are hired based on their score on a civil service exam. Jobs covered by civil service exams include secretarial and clerical jobs, air traffic control, and law enforcement. Postal service jobs are also granted based on an exam.

Civil service exams are designed to make sure the most qualified person for a position is hired. The exams were a response to the unfair practice of hiring relatives and friends, whether or not they were qualified for a job.

Background

Civil service exams originated in ancient China. Their purpose was to identify the most qualified people for jobs in the Chinese government. They were also meant to lessen the influence of family connections on hiring. In reality, young men from wealthy Chinese families took the majority of the available jobs. They were able to afford the many years of study that were needed to pass the exam.

Questions to Consider

Directions: Answer the questions below on a separate sheet of paper.

1. What jobs have you held? Have you done babysitting, lawn-mowing, or bagged groceries? How did you get your job?
2. How did the adults in your home get jobs they have held? Did they ever have to take an exam to get a job or to get a promotion?
3. What jobs are you considering for your future? What are the requirements for those jobs? Are any of the jobs covered by the Civil Service Administration exams?
4. What experiences have you had with exams? Have you taken proficiency tests or other lengthy exams? Do you think a civil service test would be harder or easier than those exams?
5. Do you think exams are a fair way to select people for jobs? What might be unfair about them?

Did You Know? In China today, the government employs about 5.4 million civil servant workers. Of these, about 56 percent work as police officers, tax collectors, market supervisors, and regulation enforcers. The same number of workers have gone to a junior college or higher, specializing in computers, sciences, and foreign languages. About 60 percent work for counties and townships. And about 40 percent of the workers are younger than 35 years old.

Civil Service Jobs Poster

Your Task

Your task is to make a poster about civil service jobs. You will research which jobs today require exams and locate contact information for people who wish to apply for the exams.

How to Do It

1. Use the Internet or library resources to locate information about civil service examinations in your area. Make sure to write down where you find the information. You will need that information for your poster.
2. Find five civil service jobs that look interesting to you. Write a brief job description for each.
3. Use the information you have gathered to make a poster.
4. Write a main heading for your poster. Then arrange the five jobs and job descriptions attractively on your poster. Include an illustration related to each job.
5. Place information on the poster that tells the viewer where to go for more information—a phone number, address, or Web site.

Follow-Up Activity

Hang your poster at a location designated by your teacher. As a class, discuss the various types of jobs that require a civil service exam. Discuss why these particular jobs might be filled through exams. Write a journal explaining which of the jobs you might like to have and why.

Name______________________ Date__________________ Class__________________

ECONOMIC ACTIVITY 12

Economic Indicators

For hundreds of years prior to A.D. 581, China had no central government. War and poverty were everywhere. Then, the rulers of the Sui dynasty fought and won many battles for control of the broken country. One of the dynasty's greatest efforts, building a massive shipping route called the Grand Canal, helped unite China's economy. It became faster and cheaper to ship food and goods across China. This was one indicator, or sign, of China's improving economy.

Economic indicators help businesses and the government determine which way the economy is headed. They also allow businesses to plan their future needs and actions. There are three types of indicators:

leading indicators: help **predict** the movement of the economy as a whole

coincident indicators: signals that move at about the **same time** as the rest of the economy

lagging indicators: signal the strength of an upward or downward swing in the economy **after** the movement has begun.

Directions: In the following chart, tell the type of indicator that is referred to by the newspaper headline.

Headline	Type of Indicator
1. Housing Prices Lowest in Months	
2. Retail Sales up 3% Over Last Month	
3. Business Debt Down From Last Year	
4. Unemployed Have Average Two-Month Wait Before Finding New Job: Down From Four-Month Wait Last Year	
5. Business Buying More Electronic Office Equipment, Hiring More Clerical Staff	
6. Industry Jobs Go Unfilled as Area Unemployment Rate Sinks to 5%	
7. Consumer Debt Higher Than at Any Time in History	
8. Telephone Company Reports 30-Day Backlog in Installing Business Systems	

Name________________________ Date____________________ Class____________________

WORLD LITERATURE READING 12

Ancient Chinese Poetry

About the Selection

The poet Duo Fu lived during the Tang dynasty in China. The Tang dynasty sent huge armies to conquer neighboring lands and expand Chinese territory. In this poem, Duo Fu wrote about the effects of military policies on the Chinese people.

Guided Reading

As you read this poem, pay attention to how Duo Fu describes the problems caused by the ongoing wars. Then answer the questions that follow.

Reader's Dictionary

conscripted: forced to join the military; drafted

colonize: to establish a colony

frontier: land just beyond a country's border

authority: power

desolate: abandoned; neglected

Ballad of the War Chariots
by Duo Fu

The jingle of war chariots,
Horses neighing, men marching,
Bows and arrows slung over hips;
Beside them stumbling, running
The mass of parents, wives and children

. . . .

Stamping their feet, weeping
In utter desperation with cries
That seem to reach the clouds;

Ask a soldier: Why do you go?
Would simply bring the answer:
Today men are conscripted often;
Fifteen-year-olds sent up the Yellow River
To fight; men of forty marched away
To colonize the western frontier;

. . . .

Frontiers on which enough blood has flowed
To make a sea, yet our Emperor still would
Expand his authority! . . .

. . . .

CHAPTER 12

Name ______________ Date ______________ Class ______________

Ancient Chinese Poetry

With the men from the western frontier
Still not returned, the government
Demands immediate payment of taxes,
But how can we pay when so little
Has been produced?

Now, we peasants have learnt one thing:
To have a son is not so good as having
A daughter who can marry a neighbour
And still be near us, while a son
Will be taken away to die in some
Wild place, his bones joining those
That lie bleached white on the shores
Of Lake Kokonor, where voices of new spirits
Join with the old, heard sadly through
The murmur of falling rain.

From *Chinese Literature: An Anthology from the Earliest Times to the Present Day.* Edited by William McNaughton. Rutland, VT: Charles E. Tuttle Company, 1974.

Analyzing the Reading

Directions: Answer the questions below in the spaces provided.

1. What do the relatives of the soldiers do as the soldiers march away?

____

2. Describe the problems caused by the soldiers going to war.

____

____

3. What have the peasants learned?

____

____

4. **Critical Thinking** What do you think Duo Fu thought of the ongoing battles and wars during the Tang dynasty? Support your answer with examples from his poem.

____

____

Name________________________ Date____________________ Class____________________

PRIMARY SOURCE READING 12

Stories of Marco Polo

About the Selection

Marco Polo claimed to have spent 17 years in the service of Kublai Khan, ruler of the Mongols in Asia and the largest empire in the world. Polo was a favorite of the khan, who sent him on business in central and northern China and Asia. In 1292 Polo returned to his home in Venice. He dictated the story of his travels. Here is part of his account of the city of Hangzhou, called "Kinsay."

Reader's Dictionary

compass: space or area
marvel: be amazed
contrived: planned or made
Idolaters: disparaging name for someone with different religious beliefs
edifice: building
trenchers: a wooden board or platter
gratification: pleasure

The Glories of Kinsay (c. 1300)

by Marco Polo

First and foremost, then, the document stated the city of Kinsay to be so great that it hath an hundred miles of compass. And there are in it twelve thousand bridges of stone, for the most part so lofty that a great fleet could pass beneath them. And let no man marvel that there are so many bridges, for you see the whole city stands as it were in the water and surrounded by water, so that a great many bridges are required to give free passage about it. And though the bridges be so high the approaches are so well contrived that carts and horses do cross them. . . .

Inside the city there is a Lake which has a compass of some 30 miles and all round it are erected beautiful palaces and mansions, of the richest and most exquisite structure that you can imagine, belonging to the nobles of the city. There are also on its shores many abbeys and churches of the Idolaters. In the middle of the Lake are two Islands, on each of which stands a rich, beautiful and spacious edifice, furnished in such style as to seem fit for the palace of an Emperor. And when any one of the citizens desired to hold a marriage feast, or to give any other entertainment, it used to be done at one of these palaces. And everything would be found there ready to order, such as silver plate, trenchers, and dishes, napkins and table-cloths, and whatever else was needful.

Source: Marco Polo. "The Glories of Kinsay (c. 1300)." In *Medieval Sourcebook.* www.fordham.edu/halsall/source/polo-kinsay.html

Name ____________ Date ____________ Class ____________

Primary Source Reading 12

Stories of Marco Polo (continued)

Directions: Answer the questions below in the spaces provided.

1. According to Marco Polo, how big was the city of Kinsay?

2. What types of buildings surrounded the lake?

3. What purpose did the buildings on the two islands serve?

4. **Critical Thinking** Based on Polo's description, what evidence does he provide that Kinsay was a wealthy town?

Name________________________ Date____________________ Class____________________

TAKE-HOME REVIEW ACTIVITY 12

China in the Middle Ages

During the Middle Ages, Chinese rulers brought peace, order, and growth to China. Farming and trade prospered. The Chinese were interested in science and technology which led to a number of important inventions. The Middle Ages were also a golden era for art and literature in China.

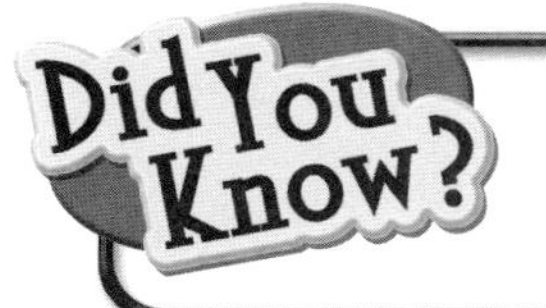

Porcelain is a type of ceramics highly valued for its beauty and strength. Today, it is often called china or chinaware because it was first made in China.

REVIEWING CHAPTER 12

China Reunites

- The Sui dynasty united China, but was short-lived.
- The Tang and Song dynasties lasted for hundreds of years and returned power and prosperity to China.
- Buddhism became popular in China and also spread to Korea and Japan.
- A new kind of Confucianism developed in China during the Tang and Song dynasties. The Chinese government supported the Confucian ideas.
- The Chinese government used civil service tests to improve itself. The examinations tested job seekers on their knowledge of Confucian writings.

Chinese Society

- During the Tang dynasty, both farming and trade flourished, and the empire grew much larger than ever before.
- Many important inventions were developed in China during the Tang and Song dynasties, including steelmaking, printing, and gunpowder.
- During the Tang and Song dynasties, China enjoyed a golden age of art and literature. Poetry, landscape painting, and porcelain making reached new heights during this period.

The Mongols in China

- Under leaders such as Genghis Khan and his sons, the Mongol Empire expanded until it stretched from the Pacific Ocean to Eastern Europe, and from Siberia south to the Himalaya Mountains.
- Kublai Khan conquered China, which led to increased trade between China and other parts of the world.

The Ming Dynasty

- The Ming dynasty rebuilt and reformed China after the Mongols were driven out. Their dynasty restored peace and prosperity to China.
- During the Ming dynasty, China's contacts with the outside world increased. Zheng He led fleets to faraway lands, and European ships began arriving in China.

CHAPTER 12

STANDARDIZED TEST PRACTICE

Multiple Choice

1. The Mongol general who conquered China was named

Ⓐ Zheng He.

Ⓑ Confucius.

Ⓒ Kublai Khan.

Ⓓ Genghis Khan.

Name ______________________ Date ______________________ Class ______________________

The Mongol Empire Under Genghis Khan, 1227

Directions: Using the map below, answer the following questions about the Mongol Empire during the reign of Genghis Khan.

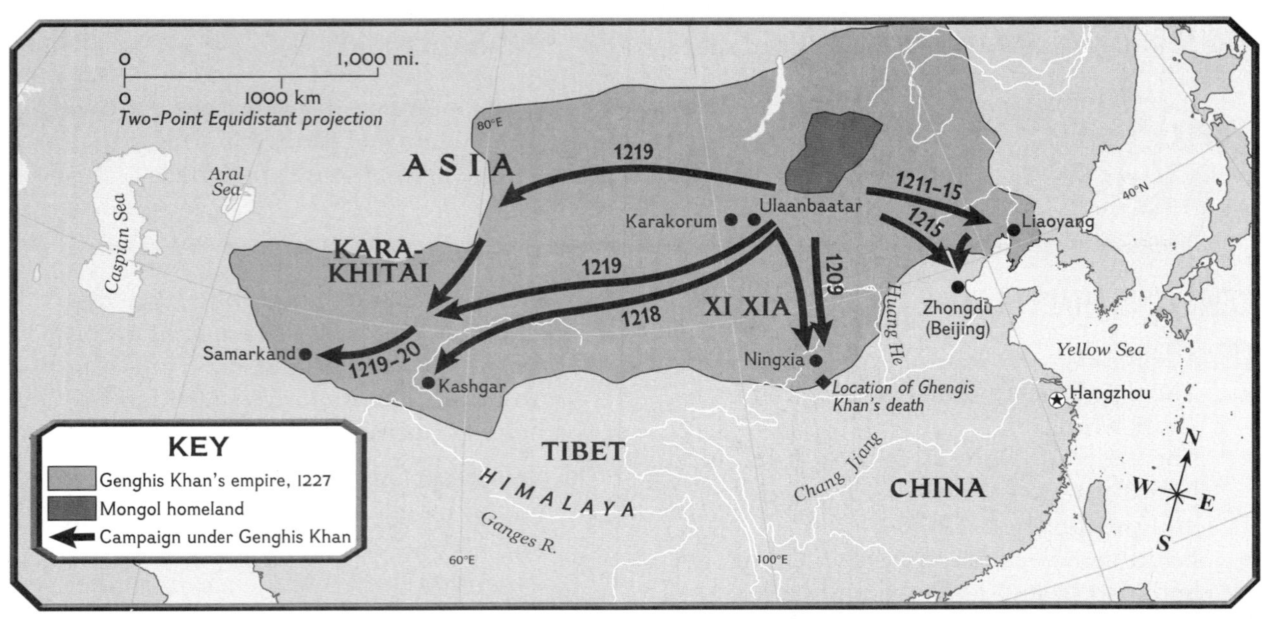

1. On what continent was the Mongol Empire located?

____

2. In what direction and toward what city did the Mongol forces strike in 1211–15?

____

3. What mountains are south of the Mongol Empire?

____

4. Locate the city closest to the western Mongol border. Name it and the year the Mongols first arrived there.

____

5. What was the capital city of China in 1227?

____

6. What sea is near Beijing?

____

7. The Mongols arrived in Kashgar in what year?

____

SECTION RESOURCES

China in the Middle Ages

Name_______________________ Date___________________ Class___________________

VOCABULARY ACTIVITY 12-1

China Reunites: Words to Know

Directions: Fill in the term for each definition listed below, writing one letter in each square.

economy	monastery	reform
warlord	Wendi	Wu

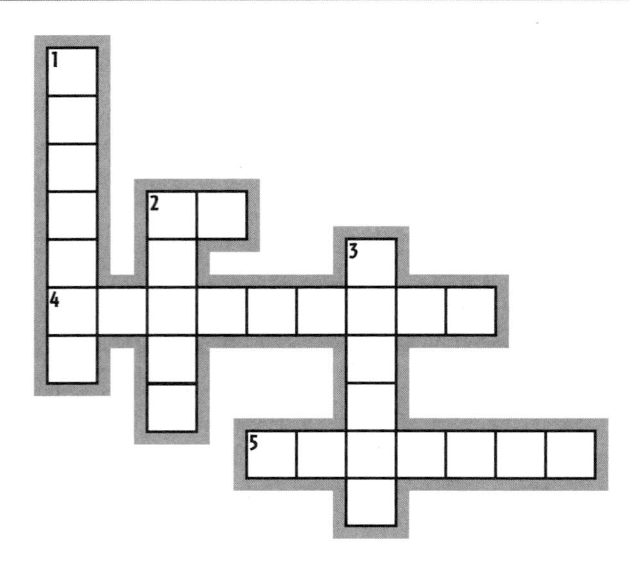

Across

2. a woman who ruled China in the late 600s

4. a place where monks lived, meditated, and worshiped

5. a military leader who runs a government

Down

1. an organized way in which people produce, sell, and buy things

2. a general who founded the Sui dynasty

3. a change that brings improvement

Building Academic Vocabulary

Directions: Read the sentence below to learn the meaning of the word *recovered.* Next write your own sentence in the space provided using a form of the word. Use the Internet or a dictionary if you need help.

recover, *verb*

Example: The Tang destroyed many Buddhist monasteries and temples, and Buddhism in China never fully **recovered.**

6. ____

____

Name_______________ Date_______________ Class_______________

VOCABULARY ACTIVITY 12-2

Chinese Society: Words to Know

Building Academic Vocabulary

create, *verb:* make, invent, or bring into being

Example: The Chinese **created** a new, stronger metal known today as steel.

Directions: The word *create* can be changed and used other than as a verb. Answer the following questions about the word *create* and its forms. You may use your textbook or a dictionary to help you.

creative, *adjective* **creation,** *noun* **creator,** *noun*

1. What is the form of *create* that refers to a person who makes something?

____

2. What is the form of *create* that refers to the thing that is made?

____

3. What is the form of *create* that describes being able to make new things?

____

4. Name at least four things that the Chinese created or invented.

_______________ _______________

_______________ _______________

Directions: Define each of the following terms in the spaces provided. Then write a sentence using each of these words and the word *create*.

5. **calligraphy**

Definition: _______________

____

Sentence: _______________

____

6. **porcelain**

Definition: _______________

____

Sentence: _______________

____

Name______________________________ Date______________________ Class______________________

Vocabulary Activity 12-3

The Mongols in China: Words to Know

Directions: Fill in each blank below with the term or name from the box that best completes the sentence. Words may be used more than once.

Beijing	**Genghis Khan**	**Khanbaliq**
Karakorum	**Kublai Khan**	**Marco Polo**
steppes	**terror**	**tribes**

The Mongols were made up of **(1)** ______________________, or groups, that lived north of what is China today. They raised animals and followed their herds as they grazed the grassy plains called **(2)** ______________________.

In 1206 the Mongols chose Temujin to be **(3)** ______________________, which means "strong ruler." His army of more than 100,000 warriors used **(4)** ______________________, or violent actions to scare people into surrendering.

In 1260 the Mongols chose the grandson of **(5)** ______________________ as the new ruler. His name was **(6)** ______________________. He moved his capital from **(7)** ______________________ in Mongolia to **(8)** ______________________ in northern China. The modern city of **(9)** ______________________ stands on the site of the Mongols' Chinese capital. **(10)** ______________________ completed the conquest of China and started the Yuan dynasty. During his reign, **(11)** ______________________ traveled to China from Venice, Italy. On his return to Venice, he amazed Europeans with stories of the wonders China.

Building Academic Vocabulary

Directions: Study the example of the academic vocabulary word below. Then answer the questions that follow. You may use a dictionary to help you.

site, *noun*

Example: Beijing stands on the **site** of Khanbaliq.

12. Define the word *site.* ____

13. Tourists like to visit historic *sites.* What are some important or interesting sites in or near your community?

____

SECTION 12-3

Name______________________________ Date________________________ Class________________________

VOCABULARY ACTIVITY 12-4

The Ming Dynasty: Words to Know

Directions: Select a term or name from the box to answer each question below. Write the term or name in the blank next to each question.

barbarian	census	novel	treason
Yong Le	Zheng He	Zhu Yuanzhang	

1. What Chinese court official made seven overseas voyages between 1405 and 1433? ____________________

2. What is the term for an uncivilized person? ____________________

3. What is the term for a long fictional story? ____________________

4. What rebel leader founded the Ming dynasty? ____________________

5. What is the term for a count of the number of people in an area? ____________________

6. What emperor built the Forbidden City? ____________________

7. What is the term for disloyalty to a government? ____________________

Building Academic Vocabulary

Directions: Circle the letter of the word or phrase that has the closest meaning to the boldfaced word. You may use a dictionary to help you.

8. When Zheng He was young, he did not know that his life would **involve** travel.

A. survive **B.** exclude **C.** require **D.** include

9. From 1405 to 1431, Emperor Yong Le sent the fleet on seven **overseas** voyages.

A. out of the country **B.** long **C.** impressive **D.** stirring

10. The Ming emperors **restored** the civil service examination and made the tests even harder.

A. accepted **B.** brought back **C.** permitted **D.** revised

Name ______________________ Date __________________ Class __________________

GUIDED READING ACTIVITY 12-1

China Reunites

Directions: Outlining Reading the section and completing the outline below will help you learn more about the reuniting of China. Refer to your textbook to fill in the blanks.

I. In A.D. 581, ________________ declared himself emperor and reunited China through battles while founding the ________________ dynasty.

A. After he died, his son ________________ became emperor.

1. He wanted to expand the Chinese kingdom, so he developed an Army to overtake ________________ but was defeated.

2. He also had the ________________ rebuilt.

3. His biggest project was the building of the ________________, the system of waterways that connected the Yangtze River and the Yellow River.

4. The ________________, who paid high taxes and had to work on these huge projects, eventually revolted and killed the emperor.

II. One of Yangdi's generals took over China and began the ________________ dynasty.

A. The rulers of this dynasty worked to improve China's ________________.

1. One ruler, Taizong, restored the ________________ to allow government officials to be hired based on how well they did on exams rather than on their family connections.

B. During this dynasty, the only woman in Chinese history to rule on her own, ________________, became empress.

III. In A.D. 960, the ________________ dynasty began.

A. This dynasty brought in an era of ________________ achievement for China.

IV. Because ________________ taught that people could escape their misery, many Chinese accepted this religion.

A. Monks and nuns lived in places called ________________.

B. The religion spread to ________________ and ________________.

SECTION 12-1

Name________________ Date________________ Class________________

Guided Reading Activity 12-2

Chinese Society

Directions: Reading for Accuracy Reading the section and completing the activity below will help you learn more about Chinese society. Use your textbook to decide if a statement is true or false. Write **T** or **F** in the blank, and if a statement is false, rewrite it correctly on the line.

_____ **1.** During the Tang dynasty, farmers were able to develop new kinds of rice that grew well in poor soil.

____

_____ **2.** People were moving northward to try to find good land to farm and to keep from dying from starvation.

____

_____ **3.** The Tang rulers built roads and waterways that increased trade.

____

_____ **4.** China traded tea and rice for silk and porcelain from other countries.

____

_____ **5.** During the Tang dynasty, trees for wood were plentiful in supply.

____

_____ **6.** The Chinese discovered steel from using coal to heat furnaces.

____

_____ **7.** Before printing was invented, books were too expensive because they were copied by hand.

____

_____ **8.** Pi Sheng invented movable type for printing that made printing much easier for the Chinese.

____

_____ **9.** The Chinese invented gunpowder that led to the inventions of the gun and fireworks.

____

_____ **10.** Chinese artists tried to paint realistic and exact pictures of landscapes.

____

Name ____________________ Date ________________ Class ________________

Guided Reading Activity 12-3

The Mongols in China

Directions: Filling in the Blanks Reading the section and completing the sentences below will help you learn more about the Mongols in China. Refer to your textbook to fill in the blanks.

The Mongols lived in **(1)** ____________________, north of China. They followed their herds through the wide, rolling, grassy plains called **(2)** ____________________. The Mongols were known for their ability to ride **(3)** ____________________ and for their **(4)** ____________________. They could shoot **(5)** ____________________ while charging at their enemy.

(6) ____________________ began to unite the Mongols as a young man. At a meeting in the **(7)** ____________________ desert, the leaders elected him **(8)** ____________________, which means "strong ruler." He developed the **(9)** ____________________ into the most skilled fighters in the world of that time. In 1211, the Mongols invaded **(10)** ____________________ and ended up controlling all of its northern region. The Mongols were known for their brutality and the use of **(11)** ____________________. Even after Genghis Khan died, the Mongol Empire expanded and reached from the **(12)** ____________________ Ocean to Eastern Europe. It was the largest empire in the world. Eventually the Mongol Empire became **(13)** ____________________ and encouraged trade.

In 1260, **(14)** ____________________ became the new ruler of the Mongols. He moved the capital to **(15)** ____________________, which is now **(16)** ____________________. He also became China's emperor and began the **(17)** ____________________ dynasty, meaning "beginning."

A famous European, **(18)** ____________________, came to visit China. Kublai Khan sent him on many **(19)** ____________________ trips, which he later wrote a book about. Under the Mongol rule, **(20)** ____________________ prospered from the trade with other areas.

Name ______________ Date ______________ Class ______________

GUIDED READING ACTIVITY 12-4

The Ming Dynasty

Directions: Answering Questions Reading the section and completing the questions below will help you learn about the Ming dynasty. Refer to your textbook to answer the questions.

1. What kind of problems was the Yuan dynasty facing during its decline?

____

2. What rebel leader became emperor after the Mongols were driven out of China?

____

3. What city did he make his capital?

____

4. Hong Wu killed officials he suspected of treason. What is treason?

____

5. How long did Hong Wu rule China?

____

6. Who became emperor after Hong Wu?

____

7. What did the Ming emperors do to increase their influence around the world?

____

8. For what three reasons did Emperor Yong Le send out his fleet of ships?

____

9. How many voyages did Emperor Yong Le support?

____

10. Who was the leader of these voyages?

____

CHAPTER 13 RESOURCES
Medieval Africa

Name________________________ Date__________________ Class__________________

ACTIVITY FOR DIFFERENTIATED INSTRUCTION 13

West African Proverbs

In West Africa, griots, or storytellers, kept alive an oral history —stories passed down from generation to generation. Many stories included a lesson about life. Proverbs are wise thoughts that contain lessons about life. The table below identifies several West African proverbs and their meanings.

Proverb	Meaning
An eye is sharper than a razor.	A look is very effective in sending a message.
A log moves only with proper tools.	You need the proper tools to carry out any task.
Sugarcane is sweetest at the joint.	Sometimes the hardest things to achieve are often the best.
He who digs a well, gets himself inside.	A person who sets a trap often gets caught in it.
Work is an obedient child, sleeping hungry is one's choice.	If you work hard, you will succeed. If you do not, you will fail.
I have betrayed a toe against a stone, let it be!	Accept the consequences of your own mistakes.
You see me dozing but I hear whatever you say.	I know what you are doing in my absence.
A favorite finger gets a ring on.	Privileges usually go to the one who deserves them.
To aim is not to hit.	Good intentions alone are not always enough to achieve your goal.
The day a monkey is destined to die, every tree is slippery.	There is no escaping your fate.
The way a donkey expresses gratitude is by giving a bunch of kicks.	This saying is used when a person is treated badly after doing a favor for someone else.
A chili pepper on its plant—how could it make you hot?	

Directions: Use the information in the table and your textbook to answer the following questions on a separate sheet of paper.

1. **Interpreting** No meaning is given for the last proverb in the table. What do you think it means?

2. **Drawing Conclusions** Which cultures do you think have a better connection with an understanding of their past: those in which stories are passed down orally from generation to generation, or those in which stories are written and read about by future generations? Explain your answer.

Teaching Strategies for Different Learning Styles

The following are ways the basic lesson can be modified to accommodate students' different learning styles.

Verbal/Linguistic Learning; Interpersonal Learning

In class, assign students to one of three groups. Ask each group to write down any proverbs or similar "teaching phrases" that their parents or caregivers often say to them. After giving the groups time to compile their lists, ask students to share the results in a class discussion. Are any proverbs common to all three groups? Do the students think the proverbs effectively convey the lessons their parents are trying to teach? Do they think they will remember these proverbs and pass them on to their children? What does this tell them about the power of the oral tradition?

Kinesthetic Learning; Interpersonal Learning

Assign pairs of students one of the proverbs and ask them to create a short skit or mime to illustrate its meaning. Students can "act out" the proverb in front of the class without disclosing which proverb is being illustrated. The class can then try to guess which proverb is being portrayed.

Logical/Mathematical Learning

Ask students to categorize the proverbs based on subject. For example, they might make several categories such as *Work, Home Life, Personal Relationships* or whatever they think appropriate. Then they should assign each proverb to one of the categories.

Verbal/Linguistic Learning; Intrapersonal Learning

Ask students to write their own short proverbs that convey the following messages: (1) The more education you get, the more likely it is you will succeed in life. (2) Sometimes it is good to be with your friends, but sometimes it is also good to spend time by yourself. (3) Even important people don't know everything; check things out for yourself. Share the best proverbs with the class.

Visual/Spatial Learning

Have students draw a four- or five-panel comic strip using one of the proverbs as the "punch line" in the final panel. The preceding panels should tell a story that sets up the appropriate use of the proverb in the final panel.

Gifted and Talented

The nyama and the nyamakalaw are oral artists who specialize in the spoken/sung word and the great power it releases. Ask students to research the importance of the griot tradition, focusing especially on the nyama and the nyamakalaw, and report their findings in a three-page paper.

CRISS Reading Strategy

Ask students to think of an event from their own lives that relates to one of the proverbs. Tell them to write two or three paragraphs describing the event and explaining how it relates to one of the proverbs.

English Learners (EL) Reading Strategy

Have EL students write and share some proverbs and sayings from their own cultures with the class.

Name____________ Date____________ Class____________

Critical Thinking Skills Activity 13

Comparing Points of View

Social Studies Objective: Identify participants' points of view from a historical and/or cultural context surrounding a time period.

Learning the Skill

A **point of view** is a person's opinion or belief about something. It is important to understand a person's point of view when you are studying history. To compare points of view, use the following steps:

- Read the material to identify the general subject.
- Identify what aspects of the issue each viewpoint stresses. Look for emotionally charged words like *never, worse,* and *should.*
- Ask the same questions about each point of view as you study it.
- Analyze how the answers to these questions are similar or different.

Practicing the Skill

Directions: In the 1300s, a Muslim traveler named Ibn Battuta visited the African kingdom of Mali. Read his account of how the women of Mali were treated, and answer the questions that follow on a separate sheet of paper.

> . . . some different customs which Ibn Battuta thought were not appropriate for good Muslims. For example, he was used to the sexes being separated. On one occasion he entered in a qadi's (judge's) house to find a young and beautiful woman to greet him. . . . On another occasion, Ibn Battuta called on a scholar and found the man's wife chatting with a strange man in the courtyard. Ibn Battuta expressed his disapproval and the man answered, "the association of women with men is agreeable to us and a part of good manners."

Source: The Travels of Ibn Battuta—A Virtual Tour with the Fourteenth Century Traveler, based on the *Adventures of Ibn Battuta* by Ross Dunn.

1. What offended Ibn Battuta about the way women were treated in Walata, Mali?
2. What did the scholar tell Ibn Battuta about why his treatment of women was not offensive?
3. Which point of view most closely mirrors your own beliefs? Does the culture that you live in influence your decision? Why?

Name ______________________ Date __________________ Class __________________

Geography and History Activity 13

Kilwa

Kilwa Kisiwani is a small island about three miles (5 km) off the coast of present-day Tanzania in Africa. On the island sits the ancient city of Kilwa. From about A.D. 1100 to A.D. 1500, Kilwa was one of the richest, most important trading centers along Africa's east coast.

A Trading Center

Kilwa was in an excellent location for trade. It sat on a deep harbor, protected from the wind by large coral cliffs. It was close to the Zambezi River valley on the mainland. That region contained salt lakes and salt springs, as well as rich deposits of iron, gold, and copper. Africa's east coast, with its mangrove swamps, abundant fishing grounds, and salt, attracted many traders from as far away as Asia and the Mediterranean.

In the A.D. 700s, Muslims from the Arabian Peninsula settled in Kilwa. Over the centuries, Kilwa gained control of the sea routes to the north and south of the island. This included the route to the port of Sofala, which had an overland trade route to gold deposits in the Zambezi region.

Gold, copper, iron, coconuts, ivory, and rhinoceros horn came to Kilwa through Sofala. Traders from India, Arabia, and the Mediterranean brought porcelain, glass, jewelry, and cloth to the island. Kilwa grew rich as it taxed the many traders who did business there. Its prosperity continued until the arrival of the Portuguese in the 1500s.

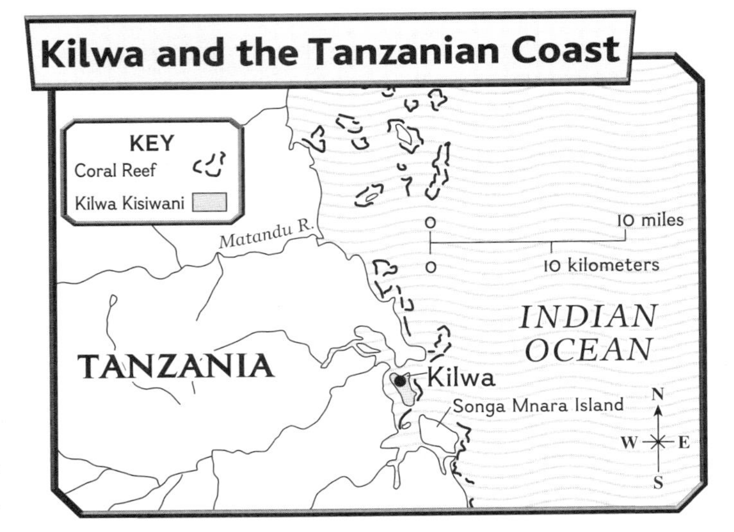

Magnificent Coral Buildings

Around 1332, the famous Arabian traveler, Ibn Battuta, called Kilwa one of the most beautiful cities of the world. What Battuta saw was a city built from the island's coral, including a Great Mosque, a number of smaller mosques, a palace, a public square, and numerous houses.

Name________________________ Date____________________ Class____________________

GEOGRAPHY AND HISTORY ACTIVITY 13 (continued)

Kilwa

The coral was cut from the cliffs along the shore and shaped into blocks. The blocks were bonded together with a cement that was made from the burning of coral. The wealthy built multi-level coral houses. Kilwa's poor lived in simple huts.

Kilwa's most stunning coral structure may have been a palace called Husuni Kubwa. Built on a sandstone cliff, the residence had more than 100 rooms and terraces, sunken courtyards, and an octagonal swimming pool. Made almost entirely of coral, the palace was said to be the most beautiful building south of the Sahara Desert. Today archaeologists are studying the remains of Husuni Kubwa and other buildings. It is hoped that the island will one day become a major tourist attraction.

Directions: Answer the questions below in the spaces provided.

1. Why was Kilwa in a good location for trade? ____________________

____

2. What trade items passed through Kilwa? From where did the items come?

____

____

3. From what substance were many of Kilwa's buildings made? How was it used in the construction?

____

____

4. What is the island south of Kilwa Kisiwani? ____________________

____

5. **Drawing Conclusions** Do you think Kilwa's location on an island gave it an advantage in trade over places on the mainland? Explain.

____

____

Name________________________ Date___________________ Class___________________

People to Meet Activity 13

Mansa Musa

Mansa Musa became king of Mali in Africa in A.D. 1312. At that time, Mali controlled the trade routes across the Sahara in Africa. Early in his reign, Musa established an empire-wide legal system. He also strengthened trade routes. A devout Muslim, Musa built many mosques in order to spread the Islamic faith.

Mansa Musa

Pilgrimage

Like all Muslims, Musa had to make a *pilgrimage,* or holy visit, to the city of Makkah on the Arabian Peninsula. His caravan included 12,000 slaves who were dressed in Persian silk and carried gold walking sticks.

Musa's caravan got everyone's attention. Islamic and European countries suddenly noticed this African empire with so much gold. Cartographers, or mapmakers, started adding Mali to their maps of the world.

Musa was very impressed with the Islamic universities and libraries that he saw during his pilgrimage. When he returned to Mali, he brought many Arab scholars with him. They helped him build great mosques, libraries, and universities throughout his empire.

After Musa built a mosque and university in Timbuktu, poets, scholars, and artists flocked to the city. Timbuktu became one of the major cultural centers of the entire Islamic world.

Directions: Answer the questions below in the spaces provided.

1. Where did Mali control trade routes? ________________________

2. What is a pilgrimage? ________________________

3. Which city became one of the major cultural centers of the Islamic world?

____

4. **Writing** Why do you think Musa wanted to build mosques, universities, and libraries in Mali? What benefits do these institutions bring? On another sheet of paper, write a paragraph answering these questions.

Name ______________ Date ______________ Class ______________

TIME LINE ACTIVITY 13

The Middle Ages in Africa (1215–1492)

Directions: Use the information in the time line to answer the questions in the spaces provided.

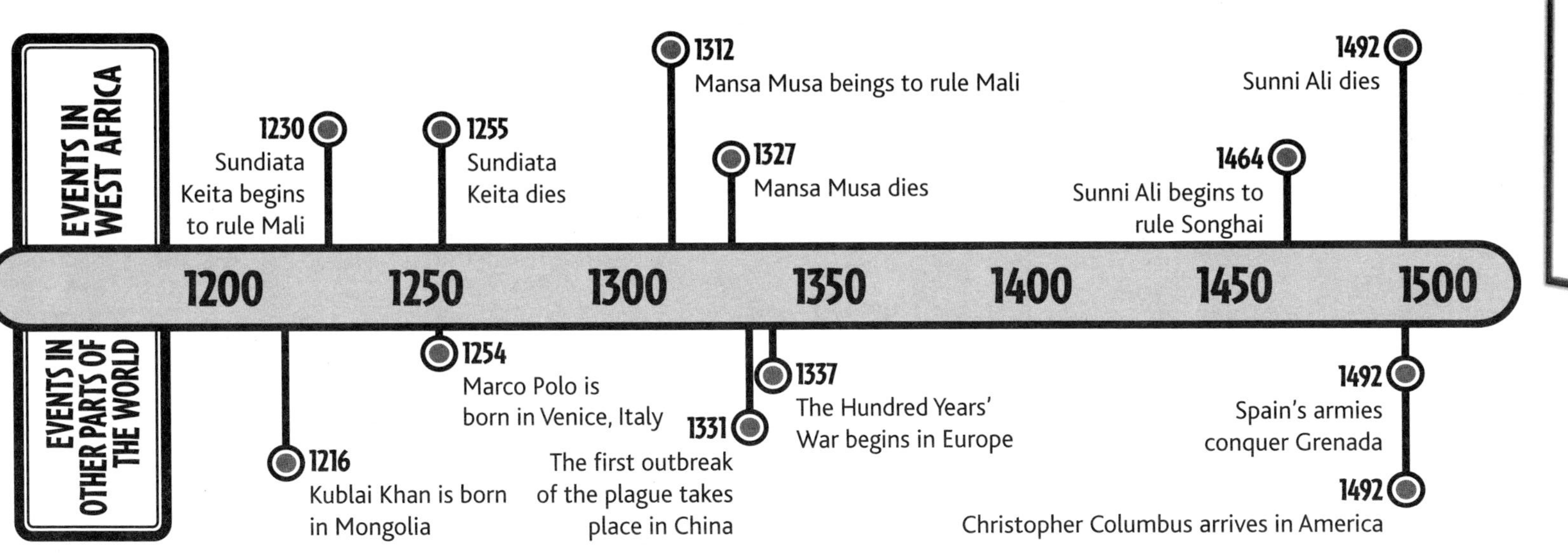

Background
From 1200 to 1500, empires in West Africa grew rich from trading salt and gold. The three most famous leaders during this period were Sundiata Keita, Mansa Musa, and Sunni Ali. During their lifetimes, important events were taking place in other parts of the world as well, as shown by this time line.

1. What was happening in another part of the world the year that Sunni Ali died?

____

____

2. What famous person was born one year before Sundiata Keita died?

____

3. Name an event that was taking place in Europe the year that Mansa Musa died.

____

4. Who had the longest reign, Sundiata Keita, Mansa Musa, or Sunni Ali?

____

CHAPTER 13

Name ____________________ Date ____________________ Class ____________________

Citizenship and Service Learning Activity 13

Cabinet Rap

Why It's Important

Much of the day-to-day work of government is not done by the president, Congress, or Supreme Court. It is done by agencies serving under the cabinet. There are 15 cabinet positions. The president appoints cabinet secretaries for all 15 departments, including the State Department and the Department of the Treasury.

The cabinet also includes a position established by President George W. Bush in 2002—the Department of Homeland Security. This department oversees the U.S. Citizenship and Immigration Service, the Coast Guard, and the Secret Service.

Background

The government of Mali during Africa's medieval period was also organized into departments. The kingdom of Mali thrived between the 1200s and the mid-1400s. It controlled extensive territories in West Africa. Royal officials had many responsibilities. One official supervised fishing on the Niger River. Another managed the forests. Mali also had officials in charge of farming and finances. Like the government of the United States, the Mali government found that dividing the responsibilities led to more efficient control.

Questions to Consider

Directions: Answer the questions below on a separate sheet of paper.

1. How many cabinet departments can you name?
2. How many cabinet secretaries can you name? Where can you find the names of the cabinet secretaries?
3. Based on the names of the departments, predict the work that the department does.
4. Which department contains the Federal Bureau of Investigation (FBI)?
5. Which department contains the Federal Aviation Administration?
6. Do you think the United States has enough departments? Which department(s) would you add? Which departments would you eliminate?

Did You Know? In addition to cabinet departments, the executive branch of government oversees several other agencies—most of which assist the president with advice and information. These include the Office of Management and Budget, the Council of Economic Advisors, the National Economic Council, the National Security Council, and the Office of the U.S. Trade Representative. The executive branch also oversees four independent agencies: the Central Intelligence Agency, the Environmental Protection Agency, the U.S. Information Agency, and the U.S. Small Business Administration.

Name_____________ Date_____________ Class_____________

Cabinet Rap

Your Task

Your task is to write a rap song or other type of song about one of the cabinet departments. You will research the work the department does, write the song, and then perform it for your classmates.

How to Do It

1. Work alone or in a small group.
2. Select one of the cabinet departments to research. Your teacher may assign one to you to make sure all of the departments are covered.
3. On the Internet, find the department's Web site. Gather some basic information, such as when and how the department was founded, who its famous secretaries have been, its current secretary, and the agencies it runs.
4. Also find out how the cabinet department to which you are assigned affects your life. Do you or someone you know receive services from it?
5. Write a rap lyric and tune that provides information about your department. Perform the song for your classmates.

Follow-Up Activity

What activity performed by the department you wrote about interested you the most? Did anything surprise you about the services provided by the various departments? As a follow-up activity, go to the jobs section of the department you studied. List at least three jobs available in the department that might interest you.

U.S. CABINET DEPARTMENTS

- Department of Agriculture
- Department of Commerce
- Department of Defense
- Department of Education
- Department of Energy
- Department of Health and Human Services
- Department of Homeland Security
- Department of Housing and Urban Development
- Department of the Interior
- Department of Justice
- Department of Labor
- Department of State
- Department of Transportation
- Department of the Treasury
- Department of Veterans Affairs

Name ________________________ Date ____________________ Class ____________________

ECONOMIC ACTIVITY 13

Decision Making at the Federal Reserve Board

The kings of West African empires had strong, centralized governments. Kings held tightly to their power controlling all trade. For example, nobody could own gold nuggets except the king. People could trade only in gold dust. That way gold remained rare and valuable and the king was able to control his empire's economy.

The withholding of funds to create value controls our modern economy, too. Congress created the Federal Reserve System, or Fed, as the central banking organization in the United States. Its major purpose is to keep the nation's money supply growing steadily and its economy running smoothly. The Fed uses some rules to achieve its goal.

Reserve requirements The requirement that banks must keep a certain percentage of their deposits as cash in their own vaults or as deposits in the Federal Reserve district bank.

- Banks must hold these reserves in case one or more banking customers decide to withdraw large amounts of cash from their accounts.

Discount rate The interest rate that the Fed charges on loans to member banks. (Banks borrow money from the Fed to maintain the bank's reserves and pay interest—extra fees—on the money they borrow.)

Directions: Use the information above to answer the following questions.

1. What is the main purpose of the Federal Reserve System?

____

____

2. The rule about reserve requirements means the bank must keep what on hand?

____

3. Why does a bank have to keep reserves of money on hand?

____

____

4. What do banks have to pay to borrow money from the Fed?

____

____

5. Why do you think the federal government wants to keep control of the money supply?

____

____

Name______________________ Date__________________ Class__________________

WORLD LITERATURE READING 13

African Fables

About the Selection

Fables are stories meant to teach children important lessons about how to behave. Many fables have been passed down by African storytellers, or griots, for hundreds of years. This fable is from Nigeria.

Guided Reading

As you read this fable, think about what lesson the story teaches children. Then answer the questions that follow.

Reader's Dictionary

cultivating: planting crops

contrary: unwilling to obey others

obscured: made hard to see

ruse: an action that is meant to mislead or trick someone

maize: corn

insolently: disrespectfully, rudely

solicitude: kindness and caring

CHAPTER 13

The Book of African Fables

The Disobedient Boy

During the planting season, Matem and her children went to the fields several hours walking from their village. They had a temporary hut where they stayed for the weeks that they were out there cultivating. When rain fell . . . they would take shelter in the hut. Matem's children were all good and willing workers, except for the eldest who was always contrary. He did not like work, you see. One night, it started raining, so they all ran towards the hut, but just when they were all inside, the entrance was obscured by an enormous ugly monster of the man-eating type.

Matem was frightened to death but she kept her head and quickly thought of a ruse: "Welcome, sir," she said breathlessly but politely. "Please come in and wait, we will roast some maize for you to eat."

The monster did not mind having an appetiser before his real (human) dinner and accepted. He sat down and waited.

"Go and find some dry matches to light the fire for our roasted maize," Matem said to her youngest.

The youngest girl ran out of the house but did not come back, since all the neighbours' matches were also wet. So Matem sent the next youngest daughter and then the next until only her oldest son was left. When she ordered him to go and find matches for the fire, he refused, insolently scorning his mother's solicitude.

African Fables

"Well," she decided. "Then I shall have to go myself."

She left the hut, rounded up her other children, and ran back with them to the village. When the monster grew tired of waiting, it devoured the only remaining food: the disobedient boy.

From *The Book of African Fables*. Jan Knappert.
Lewiston, NY: Edwin Mellen Press, 2001.

Analyzing the Reading

Directions: Answer the questions below in the spaces provided.

1. Why was the family staying in the hut?

____

____

2. What was waiting for the family when they returned to the hut when it began to rain?

____

3. What did Matem do when her son would not do as she asked?

____

____

4. Critical Thinking Why did Matem tell her children they needed to go out? What was the real reason she sent them out?

____

____

____

5. Critical Thinking Can you think of a story or fable you have been told to teach you how to behave? Describe the story.

____

____

____

____

Name_________________________ Date___________________ Class___________________

PRIMARY SOURCE READING 13

A Muslim Traveler

About the Selection

The Muslim traveler Ibn Battuta traveled nearly the entire Muslim world over a period of 30 years. His passion was to "travel throughout the earth," never twice by the same road. His journeys took him to Makkah, Iraq, Persia, the Persian Gulf, Constantinople, India, China, and more. In all, he covered more than 73,000 miles. This account provides a picture of two cities along the East African coast in 1331.

Reader's Dictionary

Rafidis: a branch of the Shiite Muslims

bazaar: a street market with shops and stalls

vast: large

unequalled: not equal

The East African Coast

by Ibn Battuta

I traveled from the city of Adan by the sea for four days and arrived at the city of Zaila, the city of the Barbara who are a people of the . . . Shafites in rite. Their country is a desert extending for two months' journey, beginning at Zaila and ending at Maqdashaw. Their cattle are camels, and they also have sheep which are famed for their fat. The inhabitants of Zaila are black in colour, and the majority of them are Rafidis. It is a large city with a great bazaar, but it is in the dirtiest, most disagreeable, and most stinking town in the world. The reason for its stench is the quantity of its fish and the blood of the camels that they slaughter in the streets. When we arrived there we chose to spend the night at sea in spite of its extreme roughness, rather than pass a night in the town, because of its filth.

We sailed on from there for fifteen nights and came to Maqdashaw, which is a town of enormous size. Its inhabitants are merchants possessed of vast resources; they own large numbers of camels, of which they slaughter hundreds every day [for food], and also have quantities of sheep. In this place are manufactured the woven fabric called after it, which are unequalled and exported from it to Egypt and elsewhere.

Source: *The Travels of Ibn Battuta,* Volume II translated and edited by H.A.R. Gibb. Copyright © 1962, Cambridge University Press.

CHAPTER 13

Name______________________ Date__________________ Class__________________

PRIMARY SOURCE READING 13

A Muslim Traveler (continued)

Directions: Answer the questions below in the spaces provided.

1. What two cities are described in this passage?

2. What do the people who live in these cities eat?

3. What types of business are practiced in Maqdashaw?

4. **Critical Thinking** Compare and contrast the cities described. How are they alike? How are they different?

CHAPTER 13

Name______________________________ Date_______________________ Class______________________

Take-Home Review Activity 13

Medieval Africa

While China enjoyed an artistic golden age, kingdoms in Africa grew rich from trading salt and gold.

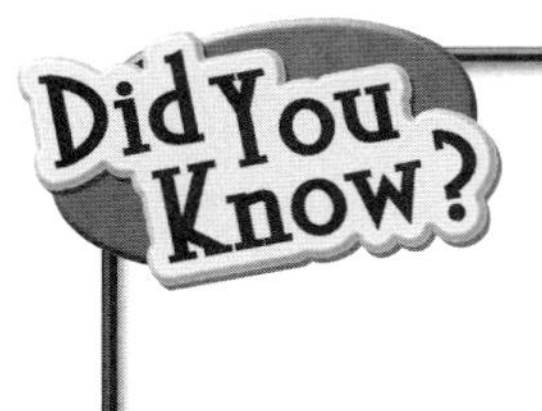

The king of Benin adorned his palace with hundreds of brass plaques, a great extravagance. The scenes on the plaques showed what the king wanted his people to think about him—that he was powerful and that he was divine. The king controlled the manufacture of brass plaques in Benin and allowed craftspeople to make them only for him.

REVIEWING CHAPTER 13

The Rise of African Civilizations

- The continent of Africa has varied landscapes, including rain forests, grasslands, and deserts.
- Beginning around A.D. 300, a succession of kingdoms, including Ghana, Mali, and Songhai, arose in West Africa. The West African empires grew rich from trade.
- Africa's rain forests blocked invaders and provided resources.
- Rain forest kingdoms, including Benin and Kongo, traded with the surrounding savanna kingdoms.
- East African kingdoms and states became centers for trade and new ideas. Trade with the Arab world helped the East African kingdoms and port cities grow.

Africa's Government and Religion

- Kings ruled the empires of West Africa. The kings closely controlled trade and divided their lands among lesser chiefs to aid in governing.
- Many African religions believed in a single creator and honored the spirits of ancestors. Religion provided a guide for living together.
- Islam became the dominant religion in the kingdoms of West and East Africa, but long-held African beliefs and customs still remained strong in many areas.

African Society and Culture

- The Bantu migration helped shape many cultures in Africa south of the Sahara.
- Many Africans south of the Sahara lived in small villages. Family was very important, and women had fewer rights than men.
- The African slave trade changed greatly when Muslims and Europeans began taking captives from the continent.
- As enslaved Africans were taken to new areas, African culture, including art, music, and storytelling, spread around the world.

STANDARDIZED TEST PRACTICE

Multiple Choice

1. The migration of what people helped shape many cultures in Africa?

Ⓐ Ghanan   Ⓒ Mali

Ⓑ Arab   Ⓓ Bantu

Name_____________________ Date_______________ Class_______________

Crossword Puzzle

Directions: Use the clues below to fill in the correct key words from Chapter 13 on the crossword puzzle.

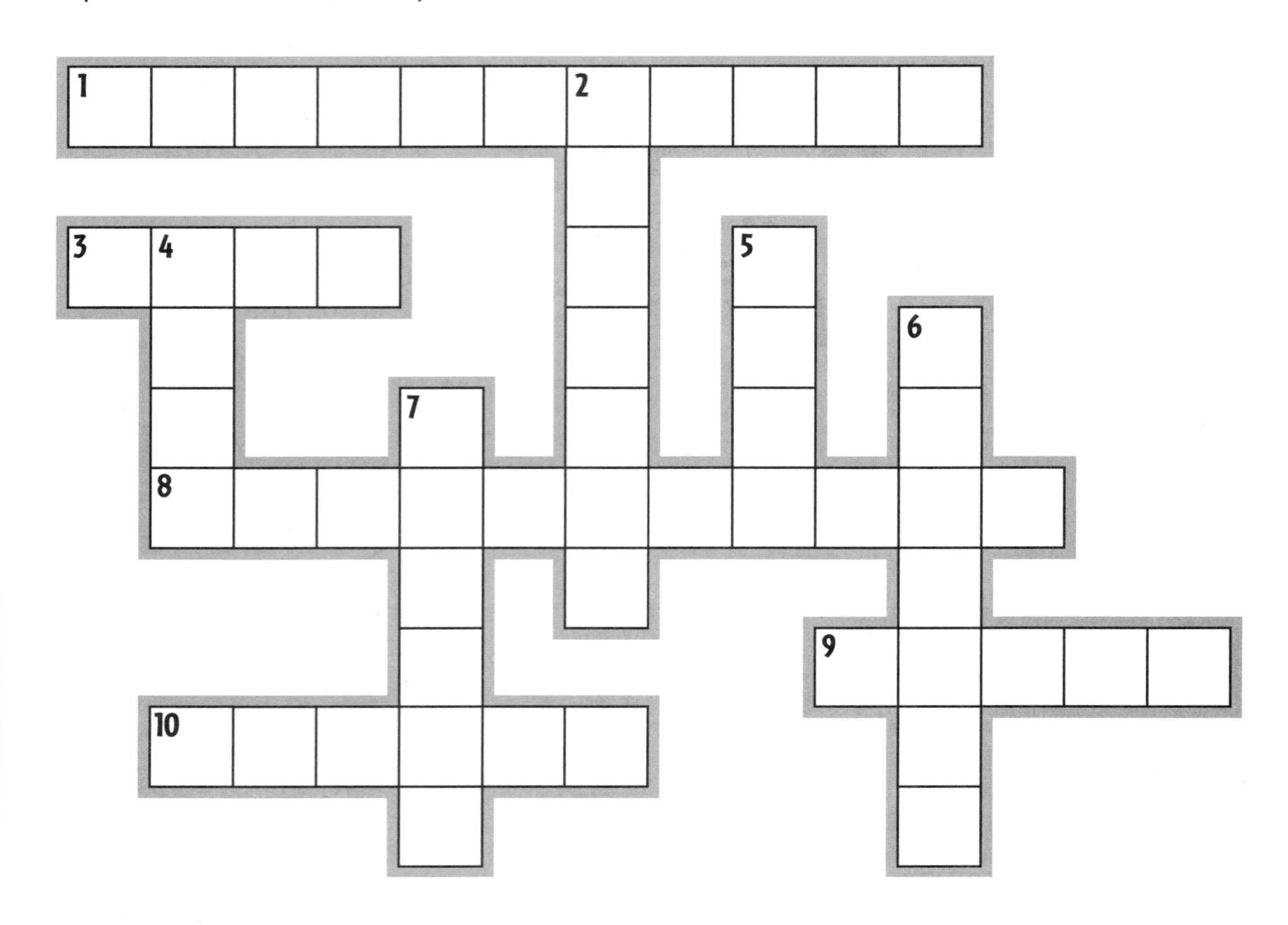

ACROSS

1. stories passed down from generation to generation
3. Mansa Musa was the last strong king of this kingdom
8. descent traced through mothers rather than fathers
9. a rain forest kingdom which arose in the Niger delta
10. a leader

DOWN

2. both the unique culture of East Africa's coast and the language spoken there
4. city-state in Abyssinia that owed its strength to its location on the Red Sea
5. a group of people descended from the same ancestor
6. an area of high flat land that almost all of Africa, except the coastal plains, rests on
7. storytellers

Section Resources

Medieval Africa

Name______________________ Date__________________ Class__________________

Vocabulary Activity 13-1

The Rise of African Civilizations: Words to Know

Directions: Write on the blanks the term or name from the box that matches each definition below.

Axum	dhow	griot	Mansa Musa
plateau	Sundiata Keita	Sunni Ali	Timbuktu

1. a West African storyteller ______________________
2. the last strong king of Mali ______________________
3. an area of high flat land ______________________
4. the "Lion Prince" and founder of Mali ______________________
5. an ancient trading center on the Red Sea ______________________
6. a sailboat used by Arab traders ______________________
7. the founder of the Songhai empire ______________________
8. important trading city in West Africa ______________________

Building Academic Vocabulary

route, *noun*

Example: Axum fought neighboring Kush for control of trade **routes** to inland Africa.

Directions: Complete the following items based on the vocabulary term.

9. What is a route? ______________________

____

10. Describe a route that you often follow, such as the route from your home to your school. ______________________

____

11. Circle the letter of the meaning of *route* as it is used in the following sentence.

After she receives the newsletter, she will **route** it to everyone in the office.

A. send **B.** forbid **C.** place **D.** start

SECTION 13-1

Name______________________ Date_________________ Class__________________

Vocabulary Activity 13-2

Africa's Government and Religion: Words to Know

Directions: True or False Print **T** or **F** on the line in front of each definition. If the statement is false, print on the blank line at the end of the statement the word that correctly replaces the boldfaced term.

Askia Muhammad	clan	Ibn Battuta
Olaudah Equiano	sultan	Swahili

_____ 1. **Askia Muhammad** was a Moroccan lawyer who traveled through the lands of Islam for almost 30 years. ____________________

_____ 2. **Swahili** is the term for the culture and language of East Africa's coast. ____________________

_____ 3. A **clan** was an East African leader. ____________________

_____ 4. **Olaudah Equiano** was a member of the Igbo who wrote about their beliefs. ____________________

_____ 5. A group of people descended from the same ancestor is called a **sultan.** ____________________

_____ 6. **Ibn Battuta** made Songhai the largest empire in medieval West Africa. ____________________

Building Academic Vocabulary

Directions: Circle the letter of the word that has the closest meaning to the boldfaced word. You may use a dictionary or Internet resources to help you.

7. Mansa Musa **granted** military heroes the "National Honor of the Trousers."

   A. denied **B.** made **C.** gave **D.** refused

8. The professor received a **grant** to do research in his field.

   A. permit **B.** gift of money **C.** degree **D.** license

Name________________________ Date____________________ Class____________________

VOCABULARY ACTIVITY 13-3

African Society and Culture: Words to Know

Building Academic Vocabulary

Directions: Study the example of the academic vocabulary word below. Then complete the activities that follow. You may use a dictionary or Internet resources to help you.

generation, *noun*

Example: African people held on to memories of their cultures and passed them down from **generation** to **generation.**

1. What is a generation? ____

____

____

2. How many generations live in your home? ____________________________

3. Use the word *generation* to describe your position in your family.

____

____

Directions: Use the word *generation* in a sentence that defines the following terms:

4. **extended families** ____

____

____

____

5. **matrilineal** ____

____

____

____

6. **oral history** ____

____

____

____

Name________________________ Date__________________ Class__________________

GUIDED READING ACTIVITY 13-1

The Rise of African Civilizations

Directions: Reading for Accuracy Reading the section and completing the activity below will help you learn more about early African civilizations. Use your textbook to decide if a statement is true or false. Write **T** or **F** in the blank, and if a statement is false, rewrite it correctly on the line.

_____ **1.** The Sahara is the world's largest desert.

____

_____ **2.** Africa is the world's largest continent.

____

_____ **3.** Besides the coastal plains, Africa consists mostly of mountains.

____

_____ **4.** The Sahara is where some of the earliest human fossils have been found.

____

_____ **5.** The Berbers were the first people known to settle in North Africa and crossed the Sahara to trade with western Africans.

____

_____ **6.** The Berbers were the first empire to develop in Africa.

____

_____ **7.** Ghana was a crossroads of trade routes.

____

_____ **8.** Sundiata Keita was a great warrior-king of Ghana that overtook Mali.

____

_____ **9.** Sunni Ali of Songhai built the largest empire in West Africa.

____

_____ **10.** Rain forests with their wet climates made farming impossible.

____

_____ **11.** Arabs invented a boat with a triangular sail to travel to Africa.

____

_____ **12.** Zimbabwe supplied gold, copper, and ivory to East Africa.

____

Name______________________________ Date______________________ Class______________________

GUIDED READING ACTIVITY 13-2

Africa's Government and Religion

Directions: Filling in the Blanks Reading the section and completing the sentences below will help you learn more about the government and religion of Africa. Refer to your textbook to fill in the blanks.

In Africa, **(1)** ___________________________ were the central part of West Africa's government. Their most important job was to control **(2)** ___________________________. People traded with **(3)** ___________________________ because the king was the only person who could own gold nuggets. In Ghana, the son of the king's **(4)** ___________________________ inherited the kingdom. Like Ghana, Mali also divided the empire into **(5)** ___________________________. One Mali king, Mansa Musa, rewarded his citizens for being **(6)** ___________________________.

African **(7)** ___________________________ varied from place to place, but all provided rules for daily living. Many Africans believed that their relatives' **(8)** ___________________________ stayed with their community.

(9) ___________________________, ruler of Mali, allowed various religions but tried to make **(10)** ___________________________ stronger by building more **(11)** ___________________________. He made Mali known throughout the world when he made his pilgrimage to **(12)** ___________________________. He helped to spread Islam throughout **(13)** ___________________________.

Under the king Askia Muhammad, **(14)** ___________________________ built the largest empire in West Africa. He made **(15)** ___________________________ a center of education and culture. He set up **(16)** ___________________________ schools to teach the **(17)** ___________________________.

The **(18)** ___________________________ culture is combination of African and **(19)** ___________________________ influences. **(20)** ___________________________ tried to destroy this culture but failed.

Name________________________ Date____________________ Class____________________

Guided Reading Activity 13-3

African Society and Culture

Directions: Answering Questions Reading the section and completing the questions below will help you learn about African society and culture. Refer to your textbook to answer the questions.

1. Why do people all across Africa share some common ideas and customs?

____

2. What formed the basis of African society?

____

3. How did storytelling play a part in the education of African children?

____

4. What are the names of two female African rulers?

____

5. What kind of slavery did the Quran not allow?

____

6. What did Europeans have enslaved Africans do?

____

7. What is the African Diaspora?

____

8. How did religion affect African art?

____

9. How did Africans use dancing?

____

10. How has African history and culture remained alive today?

____

Chapter 14 Resources

Medieval Japan

Name________________________ Date__________________ Class__________________

ACTIVITY FOR DIFFERENTIATED INSTRUCTION 14

Samurai and the Bushido

The reading below describes the samurai's Bushido, or code of conduct.

Above all, the Way of the Samurai should be in being aware that you do not know what is going to happen next, and in querying [questioning] every item day and night. Victory and defeat are matters of the temporary force of circumstances. The way of avoiding shame is different. It is simply in death.

Even if it seems certain that you will lose, retaliate. Neither wisdom nor technique has a place in this. A real man does not think of victory or defeat. He plunges recklessly towards an irrational death. By doing this, you will awaken from your dreams.

—Yamamoto Tsunetomo,
Hagakure: The Book of the Samurai

Buddhism's teachings about reincarnation and life after death helped the samurai be brave in the face of danger. Followers of Zen Buddhism, an important Buddhist sect, learned to control their bodies through martial arts or sports that involved combat and self-defense. This appealed to the samurai, who trained to fight without fear.

Shintoism taught the samurai loyalty and love of country. One major characteristic of Shintoism was ancestor-worship. In particular, the emperor was honored as a god. This belief was part of the samurais' loyalty to the emperor and their daimyo, or feudal warlords. Shintoism also taught an extreme devotion and reverence for the land of Japan. Samurais felt an intense sense of duty to Japan and its rulers.

Confucianism stressed loyalty, devotion, purity, and selflessness. These ideas were also admired by the samurai. However, the samurai did not admire purely intellectual pursuits, such as scholarship or writing poetry, which were valued by Confucianists.

Directions: Use the information in the passages and your textbook to answer the following questions on a separate sheet of paper.

1. **Summarizing** Rewrite the passage from *The Book of the Samurai* in your own words.

2. **Identify and Analyze** Why do you think the samurai rejected intellectual pursuits that were valued by Confucianists?

The following are ways the basic lesson can be modified to accommodate students' different learning styles.

Verbal/Linguistic Learning; Intrapersonal Learning

Ask students to read the passage from *The Book of the Samurai.* Then ask them to cite specific ways that Buddhism, Shintoism, and Confucianism might have influenced this particular example of the Bushido.

Logical/Mathematical Learning

Ask students to create a graphic organizer that describes the influences on the development of the Bushido.

Visual/Spatial Learning

Have students design posters that they think would appeal to a samurai in medieval Japan, based on the information in the passage. Also ask them to write a paragraph explaining why they think the samurai would admire the poster.

Verbal/Linguistic Learning; Interpersonal Learning

Organize students into two groups to participate in an in-class debate about whether an updated version of the Bushido would be good for modern American society. Students should use the library or Internet to research information for the debate. Tell students that they should try to anticipate what their opponents might say and have rebuttal arguments ready to present.

Auditory/Musical Learning

Find some examples of traditional Japanese music and play them for the class. Then have students write their own compositions, incorporating the values of the Bushido described in the passage.

Gifted and Talented

Assign students a research project comparing the samurai of medieval Japan to the medieval knights of Europe. Students should report their findings in a three- to four-page paper.

CRISS Reading Strategy

Have students Think silently about what they know concerning the values, social customs, and traditions embodied in the samurai. Ask them to Write down three to five of these facts. Have students Pair with a partner and Share their ideas. Conclude with a class Share discussion.

English Learners (EL) Reading Strategy

Have EL students identify and list any words in the passage that they do not understand. Students should then look up the words in a dictionary and record the definitions.

Name ____________________ Date ____________________ Class ____________________

CRITICAL THINKING SKILLS ACTIVITY 14

Summarizing Information

Social Studies Objective: Create and interpret written, oral, and visual presentations of social studies information.

Learning the Skill

When you **summarize information,** you focus on the main idea and the most important points. You reduce many sentences or a lot of information into a few well-chosen phrases.

To summarize information, follow these steps:

- Read the material or look at the visual information.
- Identify and make a list of the main ideas and most important details.
- Organize the main ideas and details into a concise, brief explanation. Your summary should contain the main ideas of the material in your own words.

Practicing the Skill

Directions: Study the political map of medieval Japan in 1183. It shows the feudal clans in power at the time and their territories. Then answer the following questions on another sheet of paper.

1. What important details about each of Japan's ruling clans can you list from looking at the map?
2. How did the territory controlled by the Fujiwara expand between A.D. 600 and 1100?
3. How would you summarize Japan's political state in 1183?
4. Explain what effect you think the Sea of Japan had on where the frontiers expanded.
5. In summary, which clan or clans had more power in Japan?

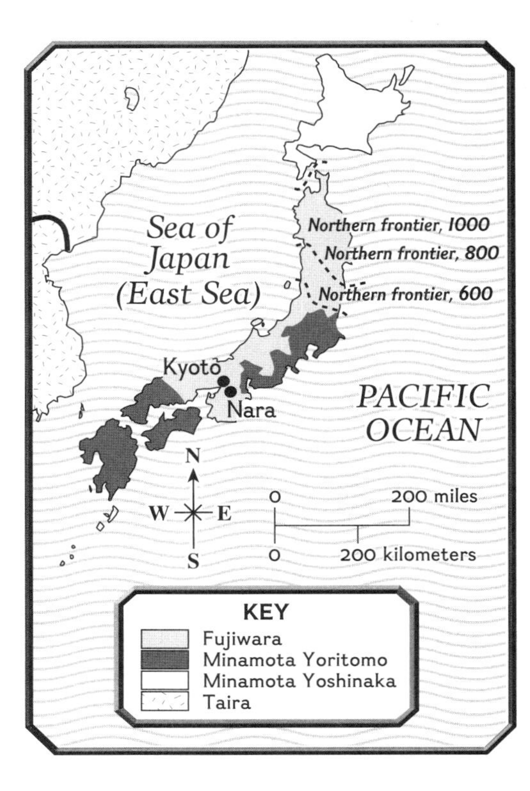

CHAPTER 14

Name ______________________ Date ____________________ Class ____________________

Geography and History Activity 14

Mount Fuji

Mount Fuji is located near the central portion of the island of Honshu, Japan. With its nearly perfect cone-shape and snow-covered peak, Mount Fuji is considered one of the world's most beautiful mountains.

Mount Fuji is an active volcano. Its first recorded eruption was in A.D. 864. Its last eruption was in 1707. Mount Fuji is considered to be a young mountain, having formed about 25,000 years ago. Another volcano is believed to have erupted over the original between 10,000 and 8000 B.C., giving the mountain its present shape. It is the tallest mountain in Japan at 12,389 feet (3,776 m).

The name *Fuji* has several possible meanings. In ancient Japanese it could mean "fire" or "deity of fire." Today it is often called "Fuji San." (When "san" is added to a name, it shows respect, similar to "mister" in English.) For many centuries Mount Fuji has been considered a sacred site by Japan's major religions, Buddhism and Shintoism. Early priests built shrines at the foot of the mountain and said prayers to keep it from erupting.

The Legend of Asama

Since ancient times, Mount Fuji's awe-inspiring beauty has given rise to many legends. In one of them, a Shinto goddess known as Princess Asama, resides inside the volcano. She is believed to have the power to make the flowers bloom and the crops grow. In order not to make her jealous, women were forbidden to climb the mountain for 1,000 years. It was feared that the volcano might erupt if her anger was provoked. This ban against women was finally lifted in 1872. On the summit of Mount Fuji is a Shinto shrine dedicated to Asama. There are also shrines to her at the base of the mountain and in the homes of many Shinto pilgrims.

According to another legend, an ancient emperor received a magical liquid that would give immortality. Afraid of its power, the emperor ordered the elixir destroyed on the peak of Mount Fuji. After that, it was believed that anyone who inhaled the smoke from an eruption would breathe in the fumes of the elixir and become immortal.

Pilgrimages to the Summit

The first recorded climb of Mount Fuji was in the A.D. 700s. A Buddhist monk made the ascent and described it as a spiritual experience. Pilgrimages to the summit became popular in the 1300s and, at various times, shrines to Shinto and Buddhist gods have been erected on the mountain. Many pilgrims still climb Mount Fuji today.

Name______________________ Date__________________ Class__________________

Mount Fuji

Since the early 1600s, a Shinto group called Fuji Ko has practiced a set of rituals at the mountain. In the beginning of July, they hold religious ceremonies at shrines at the base of Mount Fuji, officially opening climbing season. Then they make the ascent and worship at shrines at the summit. At the end of August, they hold a fire ceremony in honor of Asama, officially closing the peak climbing season. Today Mount Fuji draws hundreds of thousands of visitors from all over the world.

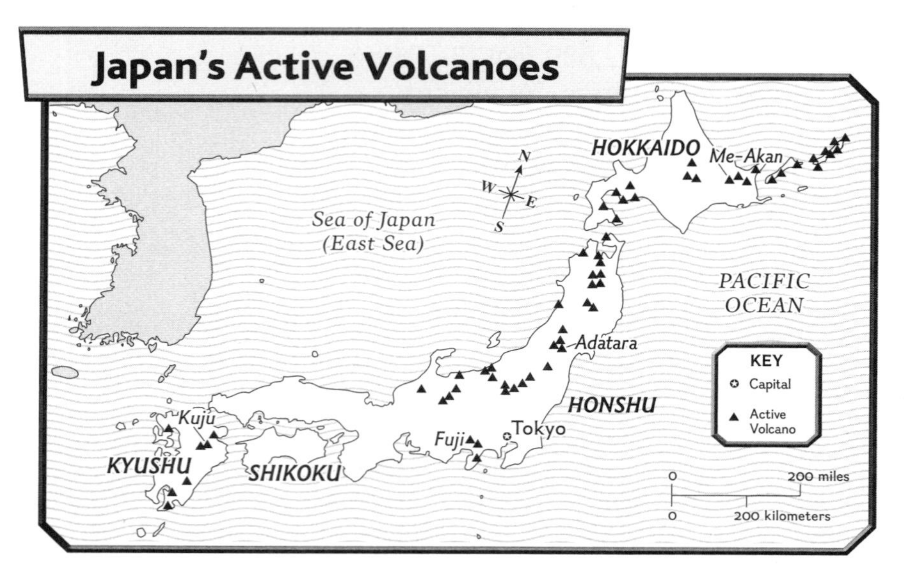

Directions: Answer the following questions in the spaces provided.

1. How did Mount Fuji gain its present shape? ______________________________

____

2. What does the name *Fuji* mean? ______________________________

3. What is the legend of Princess Asama and how did it affect worship at Mount Fuji?

____

4. To which religions do the shrines found on Mount Fuji belong? ______________

____

5. Which island has no active volcanoes? ______________________________

6. **Drawing Conclusions** Why do you think legends about Mount Fuji developed in ancient Japan?

____

Name_____________________________ Date______________________ Class______________________

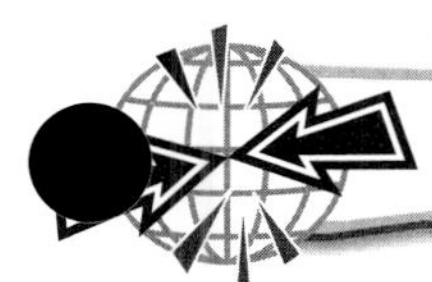

People to Meet Activity 14

Kūkai or Kobo-Daishi

Kūkai was a Japanese monk, scholar, writer, and calligrapher. In A.D. 774, Kūkai was born into Japan's upper class. He did well in school but quit when he was about 16 years old. He became a mendicant, or homeless monk. However, his writings show that Kūkai also studied at monasteries during this time.

The Shingon or "True Word" School of Buddhism

When Kūkai was 31 years old, he went to China on a government-sponsored cultural mission. While there, Kūkai studied with Master Hui-kuo, the great Buddhist teacher. Kūkai learned Sanskrit, a non-Chinese style of writing. He also studied Chinese and Sanskrit poetry, and mastered *calligraphy,* a form of beautiful handwriting.

Most important, Kūkai became a master of Shingon Buddhism. Shingon Buddhists meditate, which is the act of thinking deeply about something. They focus their meditations by using *mudra* (prayer movements), *mantra* (sacred words), and *mandalas* (pictures representing the universe).

Kūkai

When Kūkai returned to Japan, he began teaching Shingon and Sanskrit. He wrote about 50 religious works, and eventually headed several large temples and their schools.

In A.D. 816, the emperor gave Kūkai Mt. Koya for a monastery. The monastery was not finished until after Kūkai's death in A.D. 835. However, legend says that Kūkai is not dead, but is meditating on Mt. Koya.

Directions: Answer the questions below in the spaces provided.

1. What is a mendicant? ____

2. What do Shingon Buddhists use to focus their meditations?

____

____

3. Writing People who practice Shingon Buddhism learn from a teacher. Write a paragraph about the qualities that make a good teacher. For example, teachers need to be knowledgeable.

Name ____________________ Date ____________________ Class ____________________

TIME LINE ACTIVITY 14

Japan Under the Shoguns (1192–1867)

Directions: Use the background information to create a time line about Japan under the shoguns.

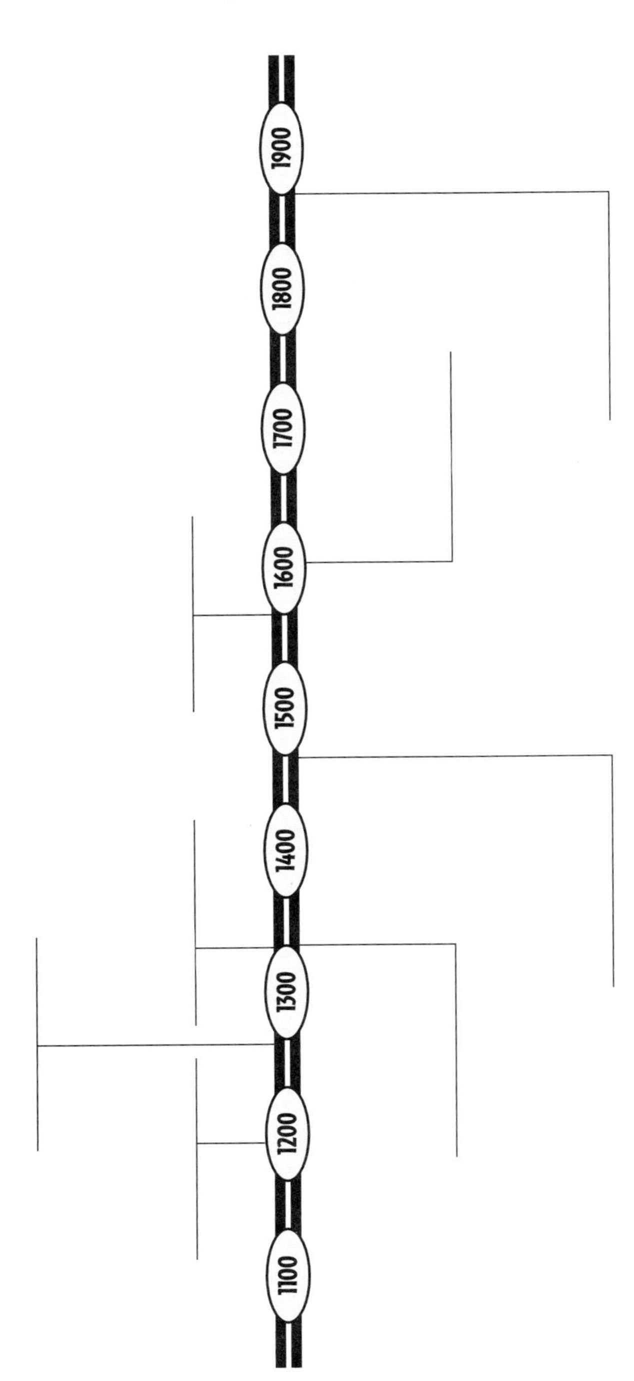

Background

In 1192 the emperor gave Minamoto Yoritomo the title of shogun—commander of all of the emperor's military forces. Japan's government was run by a series of shoguns for the next 700 years.

- Minamoto Yoritomo became the first shogun in 1192.
- In 1274, Mongols tried to invade Japan.
- The emperor rebelled against the Kamakura shogunate in 1331.
- Two years later, Ashikaga Takauji made himself shogun.
- The Onin War began in 1467.
- In 1567 the Ashikaga shogunate ended.
- Tokugawa Ieyasu founded a shogunate in 1603.
- In 1867, the last shogun resigned.

CHAPTER 14

Name________________________ Date________________ Class________________

Citizenship and Service Learning Activity 14

Armed Services Photo Album

Why It's Important

In the United States, the military is not a branch of the government. The armed forces are under the direction of the president, in the role of commander in chief. In many countries during unstable times, the military will overthrow their government. The military then puts a general or another leader in charge of the country. Such a change of government has never happened in the United States.

The armed forces of the United States are divided among five groups—the Army, Navy, Air Force, Marines, and Coast Guard. Each branch focuses on a particular aspect of our nation's security (although there is some overlap). Each group has its own traditions and uniforms.

Background

In Medieval Japan, a distinct military class developed. Between A.D. 900 and A.D. 1100, the central government of Japan weakened. Individual nobles became responsible for defending their own land. The nobles formed private armies, paying the soldiers with land. The soldiers became known as samurai warriors. The samurai followed a code of behavior called Bushido.

Samurai wore distinct battle armor made from metal or leather scales. The scales were brightly painted and laced together with silk or leather. They carried two swords and a kind of spear called a *naginata.* You can see a picture of a samurai in your textbook.

In the 1800s, most Japanese came to follow the code of behavior of the samurai. The loyalty and self-sacrifice owed by a soldier to a feudal lord became the duty of a citizen to the Japanese emperor.

Questions to Consider

Directions: Answer the questions below on a separate sheet of paper.

1. Is anyone from your family in the military? What branch is he or she in? Does your family have a history of military service?
2. What different roles do the various branches of the armed services play in peacetime? In wartime?
3. What wars have been fought in your lifetime? What peace-keeping missions have the U.S. forces participated in?
4. If you found out you were going to be drafted into the military, which branch would you prefer to join? Why?
5. What movies have you seen that show military service? Do you think the movies are very realistic?

Armed Services Photo Album

6. Have you ever spent a long time away from home? What was it like? What helped you feel less homesick?

Did You Know? The code of Bushido was followed by samurai and other warriors in medieval Japan. To follow Bushido, a warrior must be utterly loyal to his superior, maintain strict personal honor, follow a life of simplicity and self-sacrifice, and ignore pain. A follower of Bushido would remain loyal to his master even if it meant breaking the law.

Your Task

Your task is to create an informational photo album that describes the five branches of the U.S. military. You should use photos or illustrations to show their uniforms.

How to Do It

1. Work with a small group or by yourself.
2. Begin by doing background research on the five branches of the U.S. armed services. For each branch, include information on entrance requirements, service requirements, primary mission, and recent operations. Include other information that interests you. Each branch has a Web site where you can find this and other information.
3. Download photos of male and female members of each branch of the military in dress and daily uniforms and in battle dress. Mount the photos on sheets of paper the same size as your information sheet.
4. If members of your family or friends of your family are in the military, get permission to use photos of them (or make scans of the photos and print them out).
5. Label the photos. Include any information you discovered in Step 2.
6. Make a cover for your album. Hole-punch the sheets and tie them together with yarn or place them in a three-ring binder.
7. Share your photo album with classmates. Compare their treatment of the branches of the military with your own.

Follow-Up Activity

How did your photo album turn out? What would you do differently if you could do it over again? As a follow-up activity, invite recruiters from the armed services to visit your classroom to tell you about opportunities in the military. Ask the recruiter how you can contact a military pen pal.

Name________________________ Date____________________ Class________________

Economic Activity 14

Paying Taxes

During the Nara Period in Japan (A.D. 700s), the emperor's power came from his control of the land and its crops. The emperor gave his top government officials estates, or large farms, plus farmers to work the land. All people who lived and worked on land from the emperor had to pay taxes in rice or silk cloth.

Today, most citizens pay taxes. In the United States, many factors affect how much income tax you pay. The most important factor is how much you earn.

Currently, the federal income tax system has six tax brackets for individuals. These tell you what percent of your income you must pay in taxes: 10 percent, 15 percent, 25 percent, 28 percent, 33 percent, and 35 percent.

Here is how to calculate federal tax for a single individual.

If you earn more than—	but not more than—	you pay—	of the amount over—
$0	$7,150	10%	$0
7,150	29,050	$715.00 + 15%	7,150
29,050	70,350	4,000.00 + 25%	29,050
70,350	146,750	14,325.00 + 28%	70,350
146,750	319,100	35,717.00 + 33%	146,750
319,100	—	92,592.50 + 35%	319,100

Source: Internal Revenue Service

Directions: Use the table to compute the tax that would be paid by a single person on each of the following incomes. (The first one has been done for you.) Remember, to find percent you convert the number to a decimal (10% = .10) and multiply.

1. $12,000

($12,000 – $7,150 = $4,850; $4,850 × 0.15 = $727.50; $727.50 + $715 = **$1,442.50**)

2. $32,000 ____

3. $120,000 ____

4. $6,000 ____

5. $75,000 ____

6. $330,000 ____

CHAPTER 14

Name______________________________ Date______________________ Class______________________

WORLD LITERATURE READING 14

Japanese Novel

About the Selection

Murasaki Shikibu was a Japanese writer who was probably born in A.D. 973. She is believed to have written the first modern novel, *The Tale of Genji*. She also kept a diary and wrote many poems. She wrote the following set of poems after her husband died in 1001. In the poems, she describes her own grief and also the sadness her husband's daughter feels.

Guided Reading

As you read the poems, think about how Shikibu describes her feelings. Then answer the questions that follow.

Reader's Dictionary

Empress Dowager: widow of the emperor

garb: clothing

dilapidated: broken-down

Poetic Memoirs
by Murasaki Shikibu

It was the spring after the Empress Dowager had passed away. On a very hazy evening a messenger left the following poem at the house of someone who had been in mourning since the previous year:

In the Palace too
Spring brings mourning;
The sky itself
Is dark, dyed black
With the sadness of it all.

I replied:

How is it that
I wet with tears
This worthless sleeve,
In a world where all
Wear the garb of sadness.

The daughter of someone who had died saw writing that resembled that of her late father and wrote to me:

In the evening mist
The mandarin duck swims
Out of sight;
Is the child then led astray
Gazing at her father's traces?

Name________________________ Date____________________ Class____________________

Japanese Novel

The same person, seeing that the cherries were blossoming beautifully in her own dilapidated house, broke off a branch and sent it to me. I replied:

> He who grieved
> The falling of the flowers
> Already knew the sadness
> That would remain
> Beneath the trees.

From *Murasaki Shikibu: Her Diary and Poetic Memoirs*. Translated by Richard Bowring. Princeton, NJ: Princeton University Press, 1982.

Analyzing the Reading

Directions: Answer the questions below in the spaces provided.

1. Who are the two people who have died?

____

____

2. Who sent Shikibu cherry blossoms?

____

3. How did the daughter feel when she saw handwriting that resembled her father's? How do you know?

____

____

4. **Critical Thinking** Why do you think a person might grieve when the cherry blossoms fell?

____

____

5. **Critical Thinking** How did Shikibu describe her sadness? Give examples from the poems.

____

____

____

Name________________________ Date__________________ Class__________________

PRIMARY SOURCE READING 14

Diary of an Author

About the Selection

Murasaki Shikibu worked as an attendant to Empress Akiko in medieval Japan. Educated by her father, she learned the Chinese language and read Chinese literature. She became a great novelist and poet, writing over 120 poems. In this selection from her diary, she tells of the activity surrounding the empress as she gives birth to a new prince.

Reader's Dictionary

itinerant: one who travels from place to place

soothsayer: one who claims to predict the future

sutra: type of Hindu literature

oblique: dishonest or misleading

The Diary of Murasaki Shikibu

by Murasaki Shikibu

All day long she lay ill at ease. Men cried at the top of their voices to scare away evil spirits. There assembled not only the priests who had been summoned here for these months, but also itinerant monks who were brought from every mountain and temple. Their prayers would reach to the Buddhas of the three worlds. All the soothsayers in the world were summoned. Eight million gods seemed to be listening with ears erect for their Shinto prayers. Messengers ran off to order sutra-reciting at various temples; thus the night was passed. On the east side of the screen [placed around the Queen's bed] there assembled the ladies of the Court. On the west side there were lying the Queen's substitutes possessed with [or who were enticing] the evil spirits. Each was lying surrounded by a pair of folding screens. The joints of the screens were curtained and priests were appointed to cry sutras there. On the south side there sat in many rows abbots and other dignitaries of the priesthood, who prayed and swore till their voices grew hoarse. . . .

. . . Most ladies who were summoned in order that the spirits might enter into them remained safe, and they were much troubled [thinking that it would be to the Queen's advantage were they attacked]. At noon we felt that the sun came out at last. The Queen was at ease!

She is now at peace. Incomparable joy! Moreover, it is a prince, so the joy cannot be oblique. . . .

Source: Murasaki Shikibu. "The Diary of Murasaki Shikibu." digital.library.upenn.edu/women/omori/court/murasaki.html

CHAPTER 14

Name________________________ Date__________________ Class__________________

PRIMARY SOURCE READING 14

Diary of an Author (continued)

Directions: Answer the questions below in the spaces provided.

1. What types of people surrounded the queen during this time?

2. What different things were these people doing around the queen?

3. How many gods seemed to be listening to the prayers?

4. **Critical Thinking** Why does the birth of a prince cause so much joy?

CHAPTER 14

Name______________________________ Date______________________ Class______________________

Take-Home Review Activity 14

Medieval Japan

The Japanese developed their own unique culture, but looked to China as a model. Japan's emperors lost power to military leaders. Warriors in Japan were known for their fighting skills. Japanese warriors trained their minds and bodies for battle.

The *Tale of Genji,* written by Lady Murasaki Shikibu over 1,000 years ago, describes the adventures of a Japanese prince. The book has 54 chapters and over 1,000 pages of text in its English translation. It is considered the world's first novel.

REVIEWING CHAPTER 14

Early Japan

- Japan's mountains and islands isolated Japan. This isolation shaped its society.
- The mountainous islands of Japan contain little land for farming. Many people turned to the sea to make a living.
- Japan was settled by people who came from northeast Asia. They were organized into clans and ruled by warriors.
- While ruling Japan, Prince Shotoku made the emperor a strong ruler. He created Japan's first constitution and borrowed many ideas from China.
- Japan's first religion, Shinto, was based on the idea of nature spirits called *kami.*

Shoguns and Samurai

- During the A.D. 700s, Japan built a strong national government at Nara, and Buddhism became a popular religion.
- The Japanese emperors lost power to nobles and their armies of samurai. Eventually a military ruler, called a shogun, ruled the country.
- In the 1400s and 1500s, the shoguns lost power, and military lords, called daimyo, divided Japan into a number of small territories.

Life in Medieval Japan

- In medieval Japan, several forms of Buddhism, along with Shinto, were practiced. These religions affected Japanese art, architecture, novels, and plays.
- During the time of the shoguns, Japan's economy grew stronger.
- As Japan became a warrior society, women lost some of their freedom.

STANDARDIZED TEST PRACTICE

Multiple Choice

1. The first religion of Japan was

Ⓐ Shinto. Ⓒ Confucianism.

Ⓑ Buddhism. Ⓓ Catholicism.

Name________________________ Date____________________ Class____________________

Password Search

Directions: Write the words whose definitions are listed below. Use the numbers under the letters in the words to form the title of the greatest collection of tales about Japanese warriors in battle.

1. commander of all the emperor's military forces

___ ___ ___ ___ ___ ___
(letter 2: 10)

2. the bond of loyalty between a lord and a vassal

___ ___ ___ ___ ___ ___ ___ ___ ___
(letter 1: 9; letter 2: 3)

3. Japan's oldest form of poetry, an unrhymed poem of five lines

___ ___ ___ ___ ___
(letter 1: 1)

4. a holy place

___ ___ ___ ___ ___ ___
(letter 2: 2; letter 6: 7)

5. the belief that all natural things are alive

___ ___ ___ ___ ___ ___ ___
(letter 1: 5; letter 7: 12)

6. the emperor who took charge of Japan on behalf of his aunt, created a constitution, and wanted Japan to learn from China

___ ___ ___ ___ ___ ___ ___
(letter 4: 4; letter 5: 8)

7. the seaside town where the shogun set up his own government

___ ___ ___ ___ ___ ___ ___ ___
(letter 1: 13)

8. a group of families related by blood or marriage

___ ___ ___ ___
(letter 2: 6)

9. capital city built by Emperor Kammu; later called Kyoto

___ ___ ___ ___ ___
(letter 2: 11)

10. smaller religious groups

___ ___ ___ ___
(letter 2: 14)

Password phrase

___ ___ ___   ___ ___ ___ ___   ___ ___   ___ ___ ___ ___ ___
1 2 3   4 5 6 7   8 9   10 11 12 13 14

CHAPTER 14

SECTION RESOURCES

Medieval Japan

Name________________________ Date____________________ Class____________________

Vocabulary Activity 14-1

Early Japan: Words to Know

Directions: Crossword Puzzle Fill in the term for each definition listed below, writing one letter in each square.

animism	clan	constitution	Jimmu
Jomon	Shotoku	shrine	

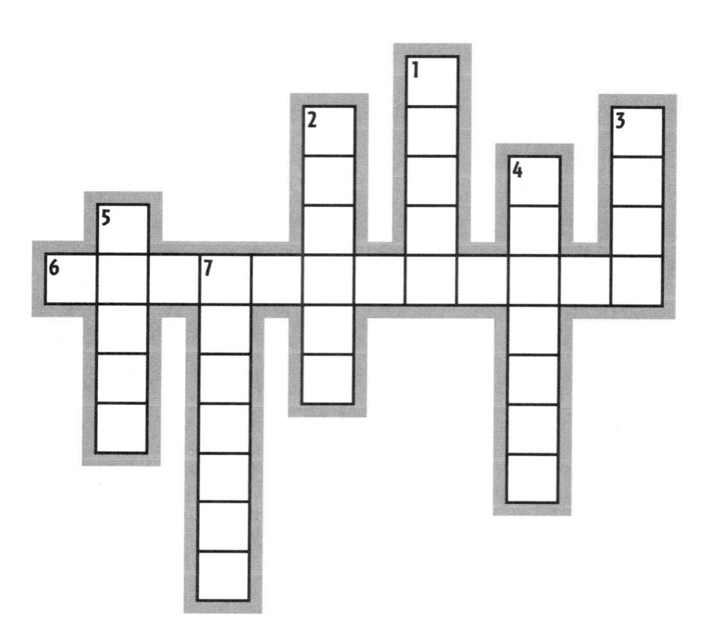

Across

6. a plan of government

Down

1. a Yamato leader who founded the line of Japanese emperors

2. a Japanese holy place

3. a group of families related by blood or marriage

4. the idea that all natural things are alive and have their own spirits

5. an ancient Japanese culture that made clay pottery

7. a Yamato prince who created a constitution for Japan

Building Academic Vocabulary

Directions: The word *isolate* is a verb in the sample sentence. In the spaces below, fill in the form of the word *isolate* that correctly completes each sentence.

isolate, *verb*

Example: The vast ocean around Japan's islands **isolated** the Japanese people from the rest of Asia.

isolator, *noun* **isolation,** *noun* **isolating,** *verb* **isolated,** *adjective*

8. Japan's location accounts for its ______________.

9. Japan's earthquake was an ______________ incident.

Name_______________ Date_______________ Class_______________

Vocabulary Activity 14-2

Shoguns and Samurai: Words to Know

Directions: True or False Print **T** or **F** on the line in front of each definition. If the statement is false, print on the blank line at the end of the statement the word that correctly replaces the boldfaced term.

Ashikaga Takauji	daimyo	feudalism	Minamoto Yoritomo
samurai	shogun	vassal	

_____ **1.** **Vassal** is the term for a Japanese warrior. _______________

_____ **2.** The commander of all of the emperor's military forces was called the **samurai.** _______________

_____ **3.** **Feudalism** is the bond of loyalty between a lord and a vassal. _______________

_____ **4.** **Minamoto Yoritomo** made himself shogun in 1333. _______________

_____ **5.** A samurai who gave an oath of loyalty to a daimyo was called a **shogun.** _______________

_____ **6.** The **daimyo** were powerful military lords who ruled territories in Japan. _______________

_____ **7.** **Ashikaga Takauji** was the first shogun. _______________

Building Academic Vocabulary

principle, *noun,* a rule of conduct or a basic truth

Example: Pledged to these **principles,** a samurai would rather die in battle than betray his lord.

Directions: The word *principle* is often confused with another word, *principal*. The word *principal* is used to mean *main* or *most important,* or *main person in charge of something.* For each of the sentences below, circle the word that correctly completes the sentence.

8. The **principal/principle** of the school was very strict.

9. The student's lack of effort is the **principal/principle** reason that she failed the class.

10. Our judicial system is based on the **principal/principle** that a person is innocent until proven guilty.

Name ______________________ Date __________________ Class __________________

Vocabulary Activity 14-3

Life in Medieval Japan: Words to Know

Directions: The alphabetical list below contains the letters for spelling the terms that complete the sentences below. Write the term that completes each sentence, and then cross out the letters used to spell the word. After you complete the sentences, rearrange the letters to spell the remaining vocabulary word. Print the word from the box and its definition in the blanks for question 6.

calligraphy	guilds	meditation
martial arts	tanka	

A A A A A A A A C C D D E E G G H I I I I I K

L L L L M M N N O P R R R S S S T T T T T T T U Y

1. Followers of Zen learned body control through ________________, or sports that involved combat and self-defense.

2. Followers of Zen also practiced ________________, which helped people to relax and find inner peace.

3. ________________, the art of writing beautifully, was much admired in Japan.

4. Japan's oldest form of poetry was the ________________, an unrhymed poem of five lines.

5. Artisans formed groups called ________________ to protect and increase their profits.

6. ______________: ____

Building Academic Vocabulary

Directions: Write one to two sentences using a form of the boldfaced word *designed*. You may use a dictionary to help you.

The Japanese created gardens that were **designed** to imitate nature in a miniature form. These gardens were carefully planned and landscaped.

7. ____

____

____

SECTION 14-3

Name______________________ Date__________________ Class__________________

GUIDED READING ACTIVITY 14-1

Early Japan

Directions: Outlining Reading the section and completing the outline below will help you learn more about early Japan. Refer to your textbook to fill in the blanks.

I. Japan is a chain of ________________ in the northern Pacific Ocean.

A. Japan is mostly covered by ________________.

B. Because only ________________ percent of Japan's land can be farmed, ________________ is an important part of the Japanese diet.

II. The ________________ people are known for their clay pottery, on which they used ________________ to make designs on the pottery.

III. The ________________ appeared in Japan around 300 B.C.

A. They introduced ________________ to Japan by growing rice in ________________.

B. They also made pottery with a(n) ________________.

C. They used ________________ as part of their religious rituals.

D. They organized themselves in ________________, or groups of families related by blood or marriage.

IV. The ________________ clan took over Japan, and ________________, the current emperor, is a descendant of that clan.

V. A Yamato prince, ________________, wanted to create a strong government like the one in ________________.

A. He created a(n) ________________, or a plan of government.

B. He ordered ________________ temples and monasteries to be built.

VI. Early Japanese believed in ________________, the belief that all natural things are alive including wind, mountains, and rivers.

A. To honor the spirits, they worshiped at ________________.

B. These beliefs developed into the religion of ________________ that still exists today.

Name________________________ Date__________________ Class__________________

Guided Reading Activity 14-2

Shoguns and Samurai

Directions: Reading for Accuracy Reading the section and completing the activity below will help you learn more about the shoguns and the samurai of Japan. Use your textbook to decide if a statement is true or false. Write **T** or **F** in the blank, and if a statement is false, rewrite it correctly on the line.

_____ **1.** During the Nara period, the city of Heian was Japan's capital and the center of government and religion.

____

_____ **2.** Like China, Japan used examinations to hire government officials.

____

_____ **3.** Japan's government carried out a census to determine who had to pay taxes and serve in the army.

____

_____ **4.** There was a time of weak emperors in Japan, because many of them were only children.

____

_____ **5.** Nobles gave land to samurai who agreed to fight for them.

____

_____ **6.** Samurai were kept very wealthy so that they would remain loyal to their noble.

____

_____ **7.** The Gempei War was a war between China and Japan.

____

_____ **8.** A shogun was a commander of the entire emperor's military forces.

____

_____ **9.** The Mongols defeated the Japanese during violent Pacific storms that the Japanese named "kamikaze."

____

_____ **10.** Feudalism is the bond of loyalty between a lord and his servant.

____

Name ______________________ Date ________________ Class ________________

Guided Reading Activity 14-3

Life in Medieval Japan

Directions: Filling in the Blanks Reading the section and completing the sentences below will help you learn more about life in medieval Japan. Refer to your textbook to fill in the blanks.

In the Middle Ages, the Japanese used **(1)** ____________________ in everyday life. Most Japanese believed in both **(2)** ____________________ and **(3)** ____________________. When Buddhism reached Japan, it had developed into many **(4)** ____________________, meaning small religious groups. One group, called **(5)** ____________________ Buddhism, preached a message of a happy life after death. Another group, **(6)** ____________________ Buddhism, taught that self-control was the way to find inner peace. This type of Buddhism used **(7)** ____________________ and **(8)** ____________________ to achieve the goal of self-control.

During this time, Japanese borrowed creative ideas for their art from **(9)** ____________________ and **(10)** ____________________. They used a shiny coating called **(11)** ____________________ on many objects. They also perfected the art of folding paper called **(12)** ____________________. Every well-educated person was required to master the writing art of **(13)** ____________________. The Japanese also wrote poems, stories, and plays during the Middle Ages.

In the Middle Ages, Japan grew wealthier due to the farming of **(14)** ____________________, wheat, millet, and barley. The Japanese also began to produce more goods that could be sold in town **(15)** ____________________ all over Japan. They also increased **(16)** ____________________ with Korea, China, and Southeast Asia.

(17) ____________________ had little power in Japanese society during the Middle Ages. They were expected to **(18)** ____________________ their fathers, husbands, and sons. In families of wealth, most **(19)** ____________________ were arranged.

Chapter 15 Resources
Medieval Europe

Name________________________ Date________________ Class________________

ACTIVITY FOR DIFFERENTIATED INSTRUCTION 15

The Book of Prisoners

Since the Tower of London was built by William the Conqueror in 1078, a record of every prisoner has been kept in what is known as *The Book of Prisoners*. Below is a small selection of some of the entries (listed with the last name first).

Date	Name	Reason for Imprisonment	Details
1100	FLAMBARD Ralph de	Extortion	Escaped in 1101 and fled to Normandy.
1106	ROBERT Duke of Normandy	Prisoner of war	Died in prison.
1196	FITZOSBERT William	Protesting the taxation levied for the rescue of Richard I	Hanged in chains.
1199	COURCY Sir John de	Rebellion in Ireland	Released after serving as English champion in a dispute over Duchy of Normandy.
1214	FITZWALTER Maud or Matilda	Rejecting the romantic interest of King John	Poisoned by an egg sent in to her by the King.
1223	ISABELLA Princess	Held pending her wedding to Emperor Frederick II	Released to marry. Became Empress in 1235.
1232	BURGH Hubert de Earl of Kent	Fell from royal favor	Returned to favor in 1234 and released.
1282	600 JEWS	"Clipping and adulterating the King's coin"	Some died in prison, many were hanged, and the rest were forced to leave England if they would not become Christians.
1288	WEILAND or WEYLAND	Inciting his esquires to commit murders	Chose to leave England forever rather than face life in prison.

Directions: Use the information in the table and your textbook to answer the following questions on a separate sheet of paper.

1. **Evaluate** In what ways were the laws of medieval England different from our laws today? In what ways were they the same? Explain your answer.

2. **Identify** Name one person listed in the table who would likely not be imprisoned in modern-day England for the reasons stated. Explain your answer.

CHAPTER 15

Teaching Strategies for Different Learning Styles

The following are ways the basic lesson can be modified to accommodate students' different learning styles.

Verbal/Linguistic Learning; Intrapersonal Learning

Ask students to select one case from the table and use the library or Internet to find a modern-day crime that is similar. Then ask them to write a one- to two-page paper comparing the sentences and explaining why people in medieval England might have enforced their laws as they did.

Kinesthetic Learning; Interpersonal Learning

Have pairs of students write a dialogue that might have occurred in one of the following situations: King John and an English noble discuss the Magna Carta; a medieval lord and an important townsperson discuss the makeup of Parliament and who should make the laws; a medieval knight and a modern American discuss the concept of "cruel and unusual punishment"; an English freeman and his lord debate the merits of the concept of the jury trial. Invite students to perform their dialogues for the class.

Logical/Mathematical Learning

Have students examine each crime in the table and rank the punishment on a scale of 1 (punishment is far too light) to 5 (punishment is far too severe). Encourage them to use library or Internet resources as needed to fully understand the crimes and punishments. After students have ranked all the punishments, have them calculate an average "severity rating" for the punishments. Invite students to share their results in a class discussion.

Gifted and Talented

Ask students to write a three- to four-page report tracing the development of law in medieval England. Students should include information about common law, the development of habeas corpus, the establishment of Parliament, and the significance of the Magna Carta. Have volunteers share their reports with the rest of the class.

CRISS Reading Strategy

Read the excerpts from *The Book of Prisoners* and make notes in your own words about five of the cases that most interest you. Use the graphic organizer format below to make your notes.

Person/People	Crime	Punishment

English Learners (EL) Reading Strategy

Have EL students name all of the people listed in the table who were released or escaped from prison.

Name ____________ Date ____________ Class ____________

Critical Thinking Skills Activity 15

Making Predictions

World History Objective: Analyze historical information by making predictions.

Learning the Skill

Sometimes you can make **predictions** about specific events or conditions based on trends and observations. Predictions of future events can be more reliable if you gather facts and observe past behaviors in similar situations. To make predictions:

- Review what you already know by listing facts, events, and people's responses to events.
- Identify patterns. Decide what the patterns show.
- Incorporate what you know and have observed with similar events.
- Make a prediction. Analyze each of the consequences by asking: How likely is it that this will occur?

Practicing the Skill

Directions: Read the paragraph below. Then answer the questions that follow on another sheet of paper.

As medieval London grew in population, their homes grew upward. These homes rose to two, three, even five stories high. To make more living space, each level of a house extended further out toward the street than the one underneath it. These homes were built of wood frames that workers hewed, or cut and shaped, outside the city and brought in by boat. . . .

Thatched roofs kept the heat in and the rain out. There were no fireplaces in early homes, only an open fire in the middle of the room with vents in the roof to let the smoke escape. In some homes an arched beehive oven was built into a corner and used for baking.

Source: Betony Toht and David Toht, *Daily Life in Ancient and Modern London.*

1. Based on the housing, how likely is it that fires were a serious problem in medieval London?

A. somewhat unlikely
B. highly unlikely
C. somewhat likely
D. highly likely

2. How would homes in medieval London withstand harsh weather conditions such as strong winds?

A. not very well
B. not at all
C. somewhat well
D. very well

3. Would you expect to find homes built in London today to be built in the same way? Explain your reasoning.

Name_________________________ Date____________________ Class____________________

GEOGRAPHY AND HISTORY ACTIVITY 15

Mont St. Michel

Until the Middle Ages, many Christians in religious orders attempted to isolate themselves from the rest of the world. One such group made their home on a small island just off the western coast of France. The monastery of Mont St. Michel used the geography of the region to create an isolated, well-protected refuge.

The waters that surround Mont St. Michel have some of the most powerful tides in the world. The only connection to the mainland is a mud flat that becomes visible at low tide. The rest of the time the rock is completely surrounded by water.

Building the Monastery

According to tradition, in the year A.D. 708, St. Aubert had a vision of an angel. The angel told him to build a large monastery at the peak of the 300-foot-high (91 m) rock that is Mont St. Michel. In 966 a Benedictine monastery was established there, and in 1020 construction of the abbey church began.

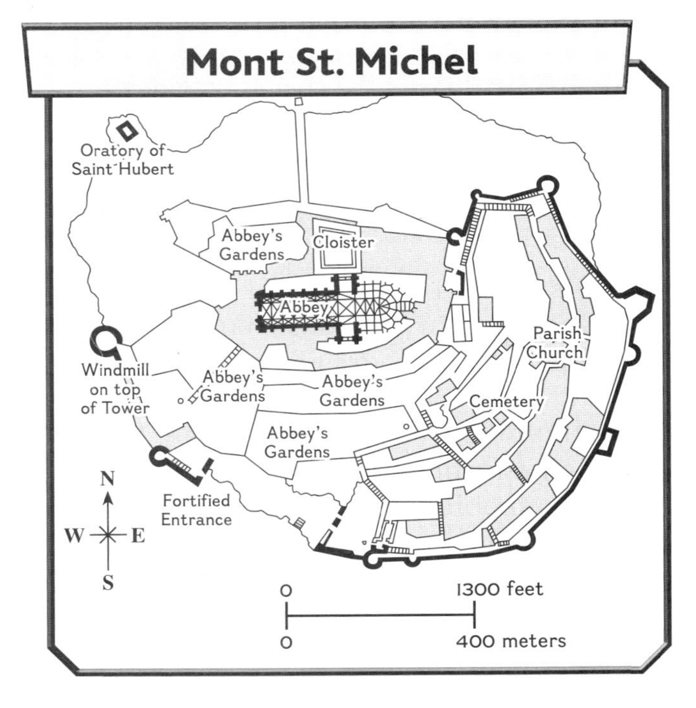

The monk in charge of the project adapted the church's design to the island's geography. Instead of leveling off the top of the mountain, he had a foundation built against the side of the mountain to support the structure.

Construction of the first abbey church took more than 100 years. Building stones were brought in from the mainland. Over the next few hundred years, the church was built higher from its existing base. Several times the base collapsed under the weight of so much stone. Following every collapse, the base was made stronger. Columns, arches, and vaults were designed to hold the structure in place, eventually resulting in the church we see today.

Name________________________ Date____________________ Class____________________

Mont St. Michel

A Safe Haven

Throughout the Middle Ages, Mont St. Michel was a destination for religious pilgrims. A small village went up outside the monastery's walls. For many years, kings and dukes fought for control of the island. During the Hundred Years' War, it was assaulted several times, but it was never captured. The tides and puddles of quicksand made an assault on the island dangerous for the attackers.

During the French Revolution in the late 1700s, the monks were removed from the island and it became a prison for those who disagreed with the government. Later, in the 1800s, the French government began to restore the island's buildings. A causeway from the mainland was built in 1880. Today Mont St. Michel is a major tourist attraction.

Directions: Answer the following questions in the spaces provided.

1. Why were early Christians attracted to the island? ________________________

____

2. How did the monk in charge of construction adapt the building to the island's geography?

____

____

3. Why was the monastery never captured during the Hundred Years' War?

____

4. How many gardens are there? Why do you think the monastery had so many gardens?

____

____

5. **Inferring** Why did kings and dukes fight for control of the monastery?

____

____

Name ______________________ Date ____________________ Class ____________________

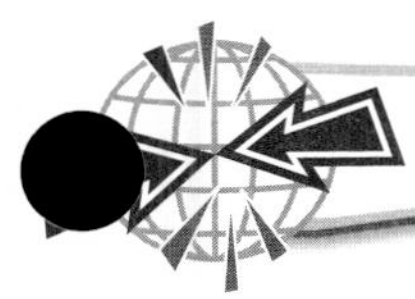

People to Meet Activity 15

Hildegard of Bingen

Hildegard of Bingen was born in A.D. 1098 in Germany. She was the tenth child in a noble family. At that time, most families "dedicated" their tenth child to the Church because they could not afford to take care of 10 children. So Hildegard was "dedicated" by her parents. "Dedicated" children became priests, monks, and nuns.

A Well-Educated Woman

Hildegard became the abbess of several convents, or religious communities of women. An *abbess* is the nun in charge of everyone and everything that is in a convent. At that time, many women were not well educated. Hildegard, however, composed religious music and wrote about art, medicine, natural history, and theology, which is the study of God and religion. Bishops, popes, and kings asked for her advice.

Visions

When she was three, Hildegard had started seeing visions. She saw flashing stars of light and glowing objects. She soon realized that other people did not see such things, so she kept it a secret.

Hildegard of Bingen

When Hildegard was about 42 years old, someone told Pope Eugenius about her visions. He encouraged her to write about them. Hildegard wrote her first book, *Scivias* ("Know the Ways of the Lord"). Her fame spread through the world. She died in 1179.

Since then, Hildegard has been beatified, or declared "blessed," by the Catholic Church. Beatification is a major step toward becoming a saint.

CHAPTER 15

Directions: Answer the questions below in the spaces provided.

1. What is an abbess? ______________________________

2. What did Hildegard write about?

____

3. **Writing** How do you think Hildegard felt when she started seeing visions? On another sheet of paper, write a paragraph about this.

Name________________________ Date__________________ Class__________________

TIME LINE ACTIVITY 15

The Spread of the Black Death (A.D. 1346–1353)

Directions: Use the background information to create a time line that traces the spread of the Black Death through Asia, Africa, and Europe. Above the time line, indicate the places in Asia and Africa where the plague spread. Below the time line, indicate the places in Europe where it spread.

Background

A terrible plague, known as the Black Death, swept across Asia, Africa, and Europe in the 1330s, killing millions. The Black Plague probably began somewhere in the Gobi, a desert in central Asia. Trade between China, India, the Middle East, and Europe made it possible for the plague to spread rapidly throughout these regions.

ASIA AND AFRICA

- The plague was carried to Alexandria in 1347.
- The next year, the plague moved to Libya and Damascus.
- The following year, it reached Makkah.
- The plague erupted again in China in 1353.

EUROPE

- The plague appeared in Caffa in 1346.
- The next year, the plague appeared in Sicily.
- The following year, it reached Pisa.
- By 1349 the plague was in France and Germany.
- Two years later, it reached Eastern Europe.

ASIA AND AFRICA

1345 | 1347 | 1349 | 1351 | 1353 | 1355

EUROPE

CHAPTER 15

Name ________________ Date ________________ Class ________________

Citizenship and Service Learning Activity 15

Aid in the ICU

Why It's Important

Even a short stay in a hospital intensive care unit can cost thousands of dollars. A hospital stay also costs in other ways. The stress of having a loved one being treated for illness is difficult on the families of patients. They often spend long hours in uncomfortable hospital visitors' rooms waiting to be permitted into the patient's room for a visit.

Background

In medieval Europe, monks and nuns often helped care for the sick. Monasteries set up clinics and hospitals as part of their service to the poor. Monks and friars tended to have better educations than others in their communities. Their understanding of diseases and treatments was also better. Eventually, medicine became one of the courses of study at medieval universities.

Questions to Consider

Directions: Answer the questions below on a separate sheet of paper.

1. Have you spent much time in hospitals as a patient? What have your experiences been like?
2. Have you spent much time in hospitals as a visitor? What were those experiences like? What would you change to make the experience easier?
3. Are there hospitals in your community that are associated with a particular religion?
4. Look through a phone book's listing of hospitals. Which hospital is close to where you live?
5. What do you know about intensive care units (ICUs)? What kinds of illnesses send a patient to intensive care? How much time do patients typically spend there?

Did You Know? In the Middle Ages, physicians used leeches to treat illness. A leech is a large, flat worm with a sucker mouth. Physicians would place the leech on a patient's gums, nose, lips, fingers, or open wound. As the leech sucked out the blood, it was believed that patients would be restored to good health. Today, leeches are sometimes used to help restore circulation in a limb that has been reattached.

Your Task

Your task is to make bags of toiletries to be given out to people in waiting rooms of intensive care units. You will collect and assemble the contents of the bags and distribute them to a local hospital.

How to Do It

1. This activity will work best with a medium-sized group or with your whole class participating.

Aid in the ICU

2. Hold a brainstorming session to get ideas for what could go into the bags. Examples might be hotel-sized soap, travel-sized toothbrush and toothpaste, washcloth or paper towels, comb, breath mints or hard candy, or a pencil and small tablet. Encourage creative thinking during your brainstorming session.

3. Contact the public relations office at the hospital closest to you. Explain your plan to distribute "comfort" bags for visitors in ICU waiting rooms. Secure permission before you go any further.

4. After you have permission, evaluate your ideas. Which ones are not practical? Which items can you get easily? You should have 6–10 items per bag.

5. Decide what kind of bag to use.

6. Decide how many bags you wish to make. As a class, can you easily make 50 bags? 100? 200?

7. Donate the materials (or gather donations) and assemble the bags. Make sure to put in a card that identifies the bags as part of a service project from your class and school.

8. Have an adult accompany you to the hospital to drop off the bags in the ICU. Ask the staff where you can place the bags so people in the waiting room will find them.

Follow-Up Activity

Were you successful in getting the bags made and distributed? As a follow-up activity, check back with the ICU staff after one month. Ask them how the program is going. Are the bags appreciated? Should you make more? What changes would the staff like to see?

Name______________________________ Date________________________ Class______________________

Economic Activity 15

Predicting World Food Supplies

During the Middle Ages, Europeans invented new technology, such as the plow and horse collar, that helped increase the amount of crops they could grow. The demand for food grows every year. The most important sources of food for the world's growing population are cereal grains, such as wheat, rice, and oats. Each person consumes about 680 pounds (0.31 metric tons) of these cereal grains each year.

In some years grain production is grater than grain usage. The remaining grain is stored for future use. In years when grain production is less than grain usage, the stored grain can be used to make up the difference. By comparing the usage of cereal grains with the production of the grains, you can predict if food supplies will be large enough to feed all the world's people.

Directions: Use the information above to complete the activity. Then answer the questions that follow on a separate sheet of paper.

1. Use the following information to create a line graph below to show the production and usage of cereal grains for 2001 through 2005. Connect the points of the graph to show the trend in production and use.

Millions of Metric Tons of Cereal Grains

	2001	2002	2003	2004 Est.	2005 Est.
Production	1863	1908	1835	1887	1956
Use	1897	1931	1932	1964	1988

Source: Food and Agriculture Organization of the United Nations

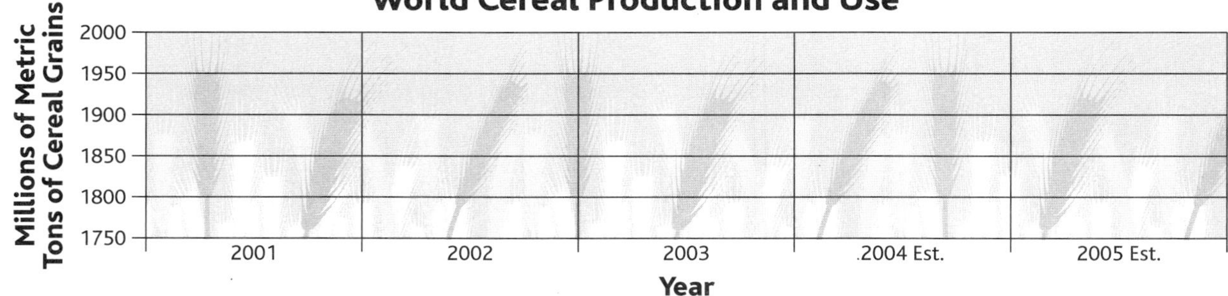

2. In what years will stored cereal grains be needed to meet the world's use of the grains?

3. What problem does this chart show?

4. What change could avoid the problem described in 3?

CHAPTER 15

Name______________________________ Date ________________________ Class________________________

World Literature Reading 15

Medieval Tales

About the Selection

The following English story was included in a 1526 book, *A Hundred Merry Tales.* Medieval comic tales like this one usually made fun of people and their habits. These stories often include a moral that teaches a lesson about right and wrong. This comic tale shows what might happen if a husband tries too hard to make his wife obey him.

Guided Reading

As you read the story, think about the relationship between the husband and wife. Then answer the questions that follow.

Reader's Dictionary

commanded: ordered

reluctant: unwilling to do something

sensible: reasonable

mad: crazy

lest: for fear that

A Hundred Merry Tales

About the Man Who Meant to Have the Pot Stand Where He Wanted

A young man recently married thought that it would be a good policy to get control over his wife from the beginning. He came to her when the pot was boiling on the fire, and although the meat in it was not cooked he suddenly commanded her to take the pot off the fire. She answered and said that the meat was not ready to eat. And he said in return,

'I will have it taken off for my pleasure.' This good woman was still reluctant to offend him, so she set the pot beside the fire as he required. Immediately afterwards he commanded her to set the pot behind the door, and she answered back and said in reply,

'You are not sensible to do that.'

But he strictly said that it must be as he required, and she mildly again did what he commanded.

This man, still not satisfied, commanded her to set the pot high up on the hen-roost.

'What?' she said again, 'I'm sure that you must be mad.' And then he fiercely commanded her to set it there, or else, he said, she would be sorry for it. She was rather frightened of upsetting him, so she took a ladder and put it up against the roost. Taking the pot in her hand she

CHAPTER 15

Medieval Tales

herself went up the ladder, asking the husband to hold the ladder firm to stop it slipping, which he did.

And when the husband looked up and saw the pot standing there high up, he said,

'Right! Now the pot is standing where I want it! . . .'

And when the wife heard him say that, she suddenly poured the hot stew onto his head and said,

'And now the stew is there where *I* want it!'

By this tale one can see that there's no sense in trying a mild woman's patience too far, lest it turn to his own hurt and damage.

From *Medieval Comic Tales*. Edited by Derek Brewer.
Rochester, NY: Boydell & Brewer, 1996.

Analyzing the Reading

Directions: Answer the questions below in the spaces provided.

1. Why did the husband tell his wife to take the pot off the fire?

____

____

2. What three places did the husband want his wife to put the pot?

____

____

3. What did the wife do when her husband said the pot was exactly where he wanted it?

____

____

4. **Critical Thinking** Explain the moral of the story.

____

____

____

Name__________ Date__________ Class__________

PRIMARY SOURCE READING 15

Thoughts of a Monk

About the Selection

In 1209, as Francis of Assisi heard Mass, the words of Jesus changed his life forever. From that day St. Francis began living simply and literally the life taught by Christ in the Gospel. Soon men joined him in what ultimately became the Franciscan order of friars, a new type of order in the church. They preached the Gospel, and worked to pay for their simple needs. In this story, St. Francis talks about the meaning of true and perfect happiness.

Reader's Dictionary

frigid: extremely cold

congealed: become solid

tunic: a long, sleeveless shirt, usually worn with a belt

Crosiers: a religious order

On True and Perfect Gladness

But what is true gladness? I return from Perugia and in the dead of night I come here and it is winter time, muddy and what is more, so frigid, that icicles have congealed at the edge of my tunic and they always pierce my shins, and blood comes forth from such wounds. And entirely (covered) with mud and in the cold and ice, I come to the gate, and after I knock for a long time and call, there comes a friar and he asks: "Who is it? I respond: "Friar Francis." And he says: "Go away; it is not a decent hour for traveling; you shall not enter." And again he would respond to (me) insisting: "Go away; you are a simpleton and an idiot; you do not measure up to us; we are so many and such men, that we are not in need of you!" And I stand again at the gate and I say: "For the love *(amor)* of God take me in this night." And he would respond: "I will not! Go away to the place of Crosiers and ask there." I say to you that if I will have had patience and will not have been disturbed, that in this is true gladness and true virtue and soundness of soul.

Source: St. Francis of Assisi. "On True and Perfect Gladness." In *The Writings of St. Francis of Assisi.* Ed. Fr. Kajetan Esser, O.F.M. www.franciscan-archive.org

Name______________________________ Date______________________ Class______________________

PRIMARY SOURCE READING 15

Thoughts of a Monk (continued)

Directions: Answer the questions below in the spaces provided.

1. What things, according to Saint Francis, bring true gladness?

2. What is Saint Francis's condition when he knocks on the gate?

3. Who refuses to let Saint Francis in?

4. **Critical Thinking** What conclusions can you draw about Saint Francis from his definition of perfect gladness?

CHAPTER 15

SECTION RESOURCES

Medieval Europe

Name________________________ Date____________________ Class____________________

Vocabulary Activity 15-1

The Early Middle Ages: Words to Know

Directions: Select a term or name from the box to answer each question below. Write the term or name in the blank next to each question.

Charlemagne	Charles Martel	Clovis
concordat	excommunicate	fjords
Gregory the Great	missionaries	Otto I

1. What is the term for people who are sent out to teach their religion?

____

2. What person's name means "Charles the Great"? ____________________

3. Who was the first Catholic king of the Franks? ____________________

4. What term means to exclude a person from church membership?

____

5. Who was the first emperor of the Holy Roman Empire? ____________________

6. What is an agreement between the pope and the ruler of a country called? ____________________

7. What pope sent 40 monks to Britain to teach Christianity? ____________________

8. What "mayor of the palace" defeated the Muslims at the Battle of Tours? ____________________

9. What term refers to steep-sided valleys that are inlets of the sea?

____

Building Academic Vocabulary

Directions: Use a dictionary to help you fill in the blank with the correct form of the word below. Then circle the letter of the word(s) that has the closest meaning to the word.

enabled, *verb* **enabling,** *verb* **enabler,** *noun*

10. Wide rivers kept people separated and __________ different cultures to develop.

A. forced **B.** selecting **C.** allowed **D.** obligated

SECTION 15-1

Name ______________________ Date ____________________ Class ____________________

Vocabulary Activity 15-2

Feudalism: Words to Know

Directions: Fill in the term for each definition listed below, writing one letter in each square.

feudalism	fief	guild
knight	serf	vassal

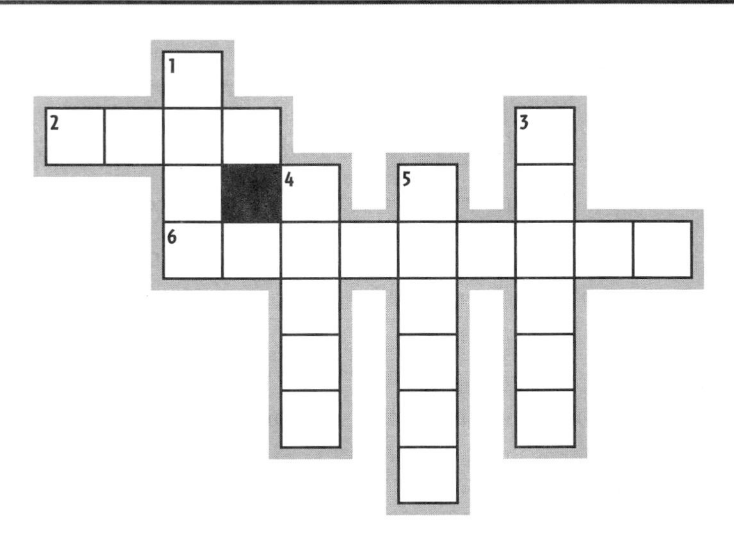

Across

2. land granted to a vassal

6. a system in which nobles ruled and protected people in return for service

Down

1. a peasant who could not leave the manor without the lord's approval

3. a warrior in armor who fought on horseback

4. a business group organized by crafts-people

5. a noble who served a lord of higher rank

Building Academic Vocabulary

Directions: Circle the letter of the word that has the closest meaning to the boldfaced word. Then write your own sentence using the word. You may use a dictionary to help you.

7. Serfs had to give a **portion** of their own crops to the lord.

A. seed **B.** harvest **C.** part **D.** twopence

8. ____

____

Name____________________ Date________________ Class________________

VOCABULARY ACTIVITY 15-3

Kingdoms and Crusades: Words to Know

Directions: True or False Print **T** or **F** on the line in front of each definition. If the statement is false, print on the blank line at the end of the statement the word that correctly replaces the boldfaced term.

clergy	grand jury	King John	Philip II
Saladin	trial jury	William the Conqueror	

_____ **1.** A **trial jury** decides whether people should be accused of a crime. ____________________

_____ **2.** **Saladin** was a ruler of Egypt who defeated the Christians and captured Jerusalem. ____________________

_____ **3.** **William the Conqueror** was the king of France from 1180 to 1223. ____________________

_____ **4.** People who have been ordained as priests are called the **clergy.** ____________________

_____ **5.** **King John** was the king of England who took a census called the Domesday Book. ____________________

_____ **6.** A **grand jury** decides whether an accused person is innocent or guilty. ____________________

_____ **7.** **William the Conqueror** signed the Magna Carta. ____________________

Building Academic Vocabulary

guarantee, *verb and noun*

Example: Many nobles refused to obey King John unless he agreed to **guarantee** certain rights.

Directions: Answer the following questions to learn more about the word *guarantee*. You may use a dictionary or Internet resources to help you.

8. What is a guarantee? ____

____

9. How is a guarantee different from a promise? ____

____

Name______________________________ Date________________________ Class____________________

Vocabulary Activity 15-4

The Church and Society: Words to Know

Directions: The alphabetical list below contains the letters for spelling the terms that complete the sentences below. Write the term that completes each sentence, and then cross out the letters used to spell the word. After you complete the sentences, rearrange the letters to spell the remaining vocabulary word. Print the word and its definition in the blanks for question 6.

anti-Semitism	**heresy**	**scholasticism**
theology	**vernacular**	

A A A A A C C C E E E E E G H H H
I I I I I L L L M M M M N N O O O
R R R S S S S S S S S T T T T U V Y Y

1. The Church tried to put an end to ______________________, or religious beliefs that conflict with Church teachings.
2. In ______________________, followers used reason to explore questions of faith.
3. A local language that is used everyday is called the ______________________.
4. ______________________ is the study of religion and God.
5. Hatred of Jews is known as ____________________.
6. ______________: ____

Building Academic Vocabulary

summary, *noun*

Example: Thomas Aquinas wrote *Summa Theologica*, a **summary** of knowledge on theology.

Directions: Answer the following questions to learn more about the word *summary*. You may use a dictionary or Internet resources to help you.

7. What is a summary? ____

____

8. When do you use summaries? ____

____

____

Name______________________________ Date______________________ Class______________________

VOCABULARY ACTIVITY 15-5

The Late Middle Ages: Words to Know

Directions: Fill in each blank below with the term or name from the box that best completes the sentence. Words may be used more than once.

Ferdinand of Aragon	Isabella of Castile	Joan of Arc
plague	*Reconquista*	

In the 1300s, a **(1)** ________________, known as the Black Death, swept across Europe and Asia. A **(2)** ________________ is a disease that spreads quickly and kills many people.

In 1429 a French peasant girl told Charles, the French prince, that her favorite saints had urged her to free France from the English. Charles became king, but the English captured the girl, and she was burned at the stake. She later became known as **(3)** ________________.

During the Middle Ages, Muslims ruled most of the Iberian Peninsula, where Spain and Portugal are today. Most Christians, however, opposed Muslim rule. Their struggle to take back the Iberian Peninsula was called the **(4)** ________________. In 1469 Princess **(5)** ________________ married Prince **(6)** ________________. They later became king and queen and joined their lands into one country called Spain. In 1492 their armies conquered Granada and drove the Muslims from Spain.

Building Academic Vocabulary

Directions: Study the example of the academic vocabulary word below. Then answer the questions that follow. You may use a dictionary to help.

vision, *noun*

Example: When Joan of Arc was 13, she began having **visions** of saints.

7. What does the word *vision* mean in the example sentence? ________________________________

____

8. What does the word *vision* mean in the following sentence?
The mayor had a *vision* for a better city. ____

____

Name________________________ Date__________________ Class__________________

Guided Reading Activity 15-1

The Early Middle Ages

Directions: Answering Questions Reading the section and completing the questions below will help you learn about the early Middle Ages of Europe. Refer to your textbook to answer the questions.

1. Why were the rivers of Europe important?

   ____

2. Who were the people living in southeastern Britain when the Angles and the Saxons invaded that area?

   ____

3. Why did the Franks become Catholic?

   ____

4. How did Christianity remain Western Europe's major religion?

   ____

5. Who was crowned the "new" Roman emperor in A.D. 800?

   ____

6. Why was the new Roman emperor concerned about his crowning by the pope?

   ____

7. Where did the Vikings come from?

   ____

8. Why was Otto I declared the Roman emperor?

   ____

9. What was Otto's territory known as?

   ____

10. Why did Gregory the Great want monks to become missionaries?

    ____

11. What role did monasteries play in Europe?

    ____

12. What was the Concordat of Worms?

    ____

Name____________________ Date_______________ Class_______________

GUIDED READING ACTIVITY 15-2

Feudalism

Directions: Reading for Accuracy Reading the section and completing the activity below will help you learn more about feudalism in medieval Europe. Use your textbook to decide if a statement is true or false. Write **T** or **F** in the blank, and if a statement is false, rewrite it correctly on the line.

_____ **1.** During the A.D. 800s, the power in government transferred to nobles instead of kings.

_____ **2.** At the center of a feudal territory was usually a city.

_____ **3.** Lords granted land called a fief for service in their army.

_____ **4.** The invention of metal armor allowed knights to ride horses.

_____ **5.** Serfs were the lord's slaves.

_____ **6.** Serfs could become free if they ran away and lived in towns for more than one year.

_____ **7.** The invention of the oxen collar improved farming because oxen could plow much faster than horses.

_____ **8.** The city of Venice built a large fleet of trading ships and became a major trading center.

_____ **9.** Both men and women could be citizens of medieval towns.

_____ **10.** Pollution was a problem in medieval towns.

_____ **11.** Women ran the household, raised the children, managed the family's money, and sometimes helped their husbands with their trades.

Name ______________________ Date ____________________ Class ____________________

GUIDED READING ACTIVITY 15-3

Kingdoms and Crusades

Directions: Answering Questions Reading the section and completing the questions below will help you learn about the kingdoms and crusades of medieval Europe. Refer to your textbook to answer the questions.

1. What king of Normandy took over England?

____

2. How did he control his own soldiers and keep them loyal to him?

____

3. What language did his officials and nobles in England speak?

____

4. What king developed the use of courts and juries?

____

5. What is the difference between a grand jury and a trial jury?

____

6. Why was the Magna Carta important?

____

7. What king established the Parliament in England?

____

8. What estates did Philip IV include in the first French Parliament?

____

9. Why was Moscow an important city to the Slavs?

____

10. What is a crusade?

____

11. Which crusade was a success in the campaign to free the Holy Land?

____

12. In what two ways did the Crusades affect Europe?

____

Name____________________ Date________________ Class________________

Guided Reading Activity 15-4

The Church and Society

Directions: Outlining Reading the section and completing the outline below will help you learn more about the church and society of Europe during medieval times. Refer to your textbook to fill in the blanks.

I. From 1050 to 1150, religious orders were started throughout Europe which meant more ________________ were built.

A. In the ________________ order, monks farmed as well as worshiped and prayed.

1. A famous monk, ________________, helped support the Second Crusade and shielded the poor against the rich.

B. Many women from noble families entered ________________ to become nuns.

C. ________________ did not stay in monasteries, but went out in the world to preach.

D. People went to Catholic worship services on Sundays and holy days called ________________.

II. The ________________ Church was very powerful in European society.

A. The pope set up a Church court called the ________________ to end ________________, or religious beliefs that conflicted with Church teachings.

B. Church leaders also mistreated the ________________ and eventually forced them out of their territory.

III. Europe's thriving ________________ produced money for education and the arts.

A. Large churches were built called ________________.

B. The first European ________________ were built to educate scholars so that they could earn advanced degrees in law, medicine, or religious studies called ________________.

1. ________________ combined the ideas of Aristotle with Church teachings.

a. His writings on ________________, the rights people have that should not be taken away, have influenced governments today.

Name________________________ Date____________________ Class__________________

Guided Reading Activity 15-5

The Late Middle Ages

Directions: Filling in the Blanks Reading the section and completing the sentences below will help you learn more about the late Middle Ages. Refer to your textbook to fill in the blanks.

In the 1300s, a terrible **(1)** ______________________ called the Black Death moved through Asia and Europe. About **(2)** ______________________ million people died in Europe of the Black Death. The plague helped weaken the **(3)** ______________________ system by reducing the number of serfs.

The **(4)** ______________________ War was between the **(5)** ______________________ and the **(6)** ______________________ over Normandy. A young peasant girl's faith stirred French soldiers fighting in the war to take the city of **(7)** ______________________. The English later captured her and burned her at the stake. She became known as **(8)** ______________________. The **(9)** ______________________ eventually won the war, although they spent much of their money in the fight.

The **(10)** ______________________ controlled most of Spain and Portugal during the Middle Ages. The **(11)** ______________________ were against their rule and began the **(12)** ______________________ to try to take back the Iberian Peninsula. The Muslims eventually lost their land except for **(13)** ______________________.

Princess **(14)** ______________________ and Prince **(15)** ______________________ married and joined their kingdoms into the country of **(16)** ______________________. They wanted all of their country to be **(17)** ______________________. They set up the **(18)** ______________________ to try non-Christians in court. First, they focused on **(19)** ______________________, and then they turned their attention to the **(20)** ______________________. Most left the country.

Answer Key

Step Into World History Activity 4

Answers to Simulation Sheet 1

1. The number of socks in each student's home will vary. Remember that the emphasis in this activity is how to count, not who has the most socks.

2. Answers will vary but may include a physical count, asking for reports from other people, estimating, and guessing.

3. Answers will vary, but may include laundry, suitcases, on people's feet, in gym bags, and so on.

4. Answers will vary but may include mental counting, making tick marks on a piece of paper, carrying a calculator, and so on. Make sure students become aware of the mental processes they are using.

5. To keep track of colors as well as numbers would require a more complex recording method. Students may respond that they will list the colors of socks and make check marks next to the colors as they count.

6. Data tables will vary. A sample is given at the bottom of the page.

Answers to Simulation Sheet 2

1. Go to the "Select a state" box under the "State & County QuickFacts" heading. Choose a state to find population data on people, business, and geography.

2. The map is black and white. It opens with Adobe Acrobat.

3. Click on "Housing" under the "People" menu.

4. Geographic subdivisions include state, county, town, township, congressional district, and many others. Most street addresses will fall within 10–20 subdivisions.

5. The predominant color on the map is yellow.

6. Answers will vary but should include that the census is a government activity paid for with taxes, so it should be easily available to people living in the United States.

Activity for Differentiated Instruction 12

1. The East China Sea and the South China Sea formed the eastern border of Tang dynasty China.

2. Answers may vary, but students should generally perceive that one of the routes of the Silk Road passed through the Gansu Corridor. The loss of this important trade route to Tang dynasty China would have made commerce more difficult.

Critical Thinking Activity 12

1. Student answers may vary, but could include the following. Loulan was built on the shores of a lake that dried up without a source of water, people

Location	White	Black	Brown	Red	Blue	Green	Purple	Multi	Other
Sock drawer	10	8	6			2	2		2

did not remain. Another possibility is that inhabitants were killed by diseases that were spread by travelers coming in and out of the city on the Silk Road.

2. Student answers may vary, but could include the following. Loulan was a trading center on the Silk Road and connected China with the west. Perhaps traders from Western Europe had traveled to Loulan and settled in the city. They may have established businesses that traded Western goods for Eastern goods.

Geography and History Activity 12

1. The rivers of eastern China flow from west to east. The Chinese people needed a way to trade north and south.

2. between 1,100 and 1,200 miles (1,770 and 1,931 km) long

3. Beijing in the north, Hangzhou in the south

4. Many laborers died while building the canal and many people thought the canal was a waste of money and lives.

5. the Erie Canal; about three times longer

People to Meet Activity 12

1. Answers will vary, but may include that Wu created a secret police force; killed many enemies, including three of her own children; made her youngest son the emperor; became empress; hired scholars to write biographies about famous women; gave her mother's relatives powerful positions in government; invited scholars to China; built temples; encouraged artists; made the army smaller; made Buddhism the preferred state religion; took privileges away from the wealthy classes; and helped the peasants.

2. Wu wanted to change how people felt about women rulers so they would accept her rule.

3. Answers will vary.

Time Line Activity 12

Kublai Khan

1215 Kublai is born
1260 Kublai becomes the new khan
1264 Kublai Khan moves his capital from Karakorum to Khanbaliq
1276 Kublai Khan's army takes Quinsay
1294 Kublai Khan dies

Marco Polo

1254 Marco Polo is born
1271 Marco Polo leaves for China with his father and uncle
1292 The Polos leave China
1295 The Polos arrive back in Venice
1296 Marco Polo is made a prisoner

Citizenship and Service Learning Activity 12

Student answers to the Questions to Consider will vary. These questions require students to use examples from their daily lives and to think critically about issues that affect them. Students should answer the questions by using complete sentences and by supporting their opinions with logical arguments. Students should complete the Citizenship and Service Learning Activity Task by working individually or in a group as directed in the How to Do It section. At the end of the project, have students review their work by discussing any difficulties they faced while they completed the project and how they resolved those difficulties. Encourage students to explain how they would improve their work if they did this project again.

Economic Activity 12

1. leading indicator
2. coincident indicator
3. lagging indicator
4. leading indicator
5. leading indicator
6. leading indicator
7. lagging indicator
8. leading indicator

World Literature Reading 12

1. The relatives run beside the marching soldiers, crying and stamping their feet.
2. There are only women left to tend the farms, and now the crops are poor. Because there are not as many crops, peasants cannot pay their taxes.
3. Peasants have learned that having a daughter is better than having a son, because a daughter will not go far away to be killed in battle.
4. Duo Fu was against the wars. He wrote about the problems caused by the soldiers leaving, about the sorrow it caused their wives, parents, and children, and about the sadness of the spirits of the dead.

Primary Source Reading 12

1. According to Marco Polo, the city of Kinsay had a circumference of 100 miles.
2. Around the lake were palaces, mansions, abbeys, churches, and large palaces for public use.
3. The buildings on the islands could be used by citizens for wedding feasts or entertainment.
4. Student answers will vary. In general, they should consider the bridges, palaces, and mansions of the city and the lifestyle of people, with weddings and other entertainment.

Take Home Review Activity 12

Standardized Test Practice

1. D

Activity 12

1. Asia
2. East toward Liaoyang
3. Himalayan Mountains
4. Samarkand; 1219
5. Hangzhou
6. Yellow Sea
7. 1218

Vocabulary Activities

Section 12-1 China Reunites: Words to Know

1. economy
2. Wu (across)

2. Wendi (down)

3. reform

4. monastery

5. warlord

6. Answers may vary. A sample sentence would be: The patient was expected to make a full recovery.

Section 12-2 Chinese Society: Words to Know

1. creator

2. creation

3. creative

4. Answers may vary but should include at least four of the following: silk fabric, porcelain, steel, printing, movable type, gunpowder, ships with rudders and sails, the compass, calligraphy

5. Definition: beautiful characters made with a brush and ink

   Sentence: Answers will vary. A sample sentence would be: Chinese painters created beautiful calligraphy for their works.

6. Definition: a material made of fine clay and baked at high temperatures

   Sentence: Answers will vary. A sample sentence would be: The Chinese created plates, cups, figurines, and vases made of porcelain.

Section 12-3 The Mongols in China: Words to Know

1. tribes

2. steppes

3. Genghis Khan

4. terror

5. Genghis Khan

6. Kublai Khan

7. Karakorum

8. Khanbaliq

9. Beijing

10. Kublai Khan

11. Marco Polo

12. the place where something is, was, or will be; location

13. Answers will vary but should include historic landmarks, buildings, or other places of interest to tourists.

Section 12-4 The Ming Dynasty: Words to Know

1. Zheng He

2. barbarian

3. novel

4. Zhu Yuanzhang

5. census

6. Yong Le

7. treason

8. D

9. A

10. B

Guided Reading Activities

12-1 China Reunites

I. Wendi, Sui
   A. Yangdi
      1. Korea
      2. Great Wall

3. Grand Canal
4. farmers

II. Tang
  A. government
    1. civil service exam
  B. Wu

III. Song
  A. cultural

IV. Buddhism
  A. monasteries
  B. Korea, Japan

12-2 Chinese Society

1. True.
2. False. People were moving southward because rice grew abundantly in the Chang Jiang valley.
3. True.
4. False. China traded tea, steel, paper, silk, and porcelain to get gold, silver, precious stones, and fine woods.
5. False. During the Tang dynasty, wood was in scarce supply.
6. True.
7. True.
8. False. Woodblock printing was still easier to use for the Chinese because their language had so many characters.
9. True.
10. False. Chinese artists did not try to portray exact pictures, but the "idea" of landscapes.

12-3 The Mongols in China

1. Mongolia
2. steppes
3. horses
4. fighting
5. arrows
6. Temujin
7. Gobi
8. Genghis Khan
9. Mongols
10. China
11. terror
12. Pacific
13. peaceful
14. Kublai Khan
15. Khanbaliq
16. Beijing
17. Yuan
18. Marco Polo
19. fact-finding
20. China

12-4 The Ming Dynasty

1. The Mongol groups in the north were breaking away and the Chinese wanted their own dynasty.
2. Zhu Yuanzhang became emperor after the Mongols were driven out of China.
3. Nanjing was the capital in southern China under Zhu Yuanzhang.
4. Treason is disloyalty to the government.
5. Hong Wu was emperor for 30 years.

6. Yong Le, Hong Wu's son, became emperor.
7. They built a fleet of ships to increase their influence around the world.
8. Emperor Yong Le wanted to trade with other kingdoms, show off China's power, and gain tribute from weaker kingdoms.
9. The fleet went out on seven voyages.
10. Zheng Le was the leader of these voyages.

Activity for Differentiated Instruction 13

1. Answers may vary. One possible answer: The issue is none of your concern, how could it bother you?
2. Answers may vary. One possible answer: Cultures with a strong oral tradition have a greater connection to their pasts because people in these cultures continually hear and repeat the stories. This does not necessarily happen in cultures that rely on the written word for preserving stories and history.

Critical Thinking Activity 13

1. Students' answers may vary, but should include the idea that according to Battuta's Muslim customs, women and men should be separated.
2. Students' answers may vary, but should include the idea that according to the scholar, the association of men and women is acceptable and in good manners.
3. Answers will vary. Students' can agree or disagree for logical reasons, though most will probably choose the Malinese scholar's view as it reflects a more modern view of how women should be treated. Students should state something to the effect that our culture does affect the way people view other people, and would probably have an effect on which point of view they most closely identified with.

Geography and History Activity 13

1. Kilwa sat on a deep harbor where it was protected from the wind by large cliffs. It was close to the Zambezi River valley, which contained salt lakes and springs; and rich deposits of iron, gold, and copper.
2. Gold, copper, iron, coconuts, ivory, and rhinoceros horns came from Africa. From India, Arabia, and the Mediterranean came porcelain, glass, jewelry, and cloth.
3. coral; The coral was cut from the cliffs, shaped into blocks, and bonded together with a cement that was made from the burning of coral.
4. Songa Mnara Island
5. Students may note that traders could reach the island before the mainland, perhaps giving the island an advantage.

People to Meet Activity 13

1. Mali controlled trade routes across the Sahara in Africa.
2. A pilgrimage is a holy visit.
3. Timbuktu became one of the major cultural centers of the Islamic world.

4. Answers will vary, but students may write about how universities educate people, libraries store information, and mosques bring communities together at a place of worship.

Time Line Activity 13

1. Spain's armies conquered Grenada, and Columbus arrived in America.
2. Marco Polo was born one year before Sundiata Keita died.
3. The Hundred Years' War began.
4. Sunni Ali had the longest reign.

Citizenship and Service Learning Activity 13

Student answers to the Questions to Consider will vary. These questions require students to use examples from their daily lives and to think critically about issues that affect them. Students should answer the questions by using complete sentences and by supporting their opinions with logical arguments. Students should complete the Citizenship and Service Learning Activity Task by working individually or in a group as directed in the How to Do It section. At the end of the project, have students review their work by discussing any difficulties they faced while they completed the project and how they resolved those difficulties. Encourage students to explain how they would improve their work if they did this project again.

Economic Activity 13

1. The Fed's purpose is to keep the nation's money supply growing and the economy running smoothly.
2. It must keep a certain percentage of the money people have deposited.
3. It keeps a reserve in case a customer wants to make a withdrawal.
4. Banks have to pay interest on money borrowed from the Fed.
5. Answers should include that the government wants to make sure the economy runs smoothly.

World Literature Reading 13

1. The family spent several weeks at the hut during planting season, because the fields were several hours walking distance from their home.
2. A man-eating monster was waiting for them.
3. She decided to go herself, and found her other children and ran back to the village.
4. Matem told her children to go find dry matches to light the fire to roast the maize for the monster. She was really sending them out to get them away from the monster.
5. Answers will vary, but may include descriptions of fables, religious stories, or fairy tales that teach lessons to children.

Primary Source Reading 13

1. Zaila and Maqdashaw are described in this passage.
2. The people of these cities eat camels, sheep, and fish.
3. Two types of business in Maqdashaw are trade (merchants) and manufacturing (fabric).
4. Student answers will vary. In general, they should reflect on the quality of

life described. Both cities slaughter camels for food. Both have sheep. Maqdashaw seems to be more developed and larger, with a fabric trade.

Take Home Review Activity 13

Standardized Test Practice

1. D

Activity 13

ACROSS

1. oral history
3. Mali
8. matrilineal
9. Benin
10. sultan

DOWN

2. Swahili
4. Axum
5. clan
6. plateau
7. griots

Vocabulary Activities

Section 13-1 The Rise of African Civilizations: Words to Know

1. griot
2. Mansa Musa
3. plateau
4. Sundiata Keita
5. Axum
6. dhow
7. Sunni Ali
8. Timbuktu
9. A route is a road or course that travelers follow.
10. Answers will vary. Students should include streets and other landmarks along the route.
11. A

Section 13-2 Africa's Government and Religion: Words to Know

1. False; Ibn Battuta
2. True.
3. False; sultan
4. True.
5. False; clan
6. False; Askia Muhammad
7. C
8. B

Section 13-3 African Society and Culture: Words to Know

1. A generation is an age group or level (such as father, son, and grandson) in a family line.
2. Answers will vary. Most students will indicate at least two—their generation and that of their parent(s) or guardian(s).
3. Answers will vary. A sample response would be: I am the youngest generation in my family. My parents and grandparents are the older generations.
4. Extended families are families made up of several *generations*.

5. Matrilineal means tracing the *generations* in families through mothers rather than fathers.

6. Oral history refers to stories passed down from *generation* to *generation.*

Guided Reading Activities

13-1 The Rise of African Civilizations

1. True.
2. False. Africa is the world's second largest continent.
3. False. Besides the coastal plains, Africa is situated on a plateau.
4. False. The Great Rift Valley is where some of the earliest human fossils have been found.
5. True.
6. False. Ghana was the first empire to develop in Africa.
7. True.
8. False. Sundiata Keita was a great warrior-king of Mali that overtook Ghana.
9. True.
10. False. Rain forests had good, farmable soil and a warm, wet climate that helped produce a surplus of foods like bananas, yams, and rice.
11. True.
12. True.

13-2 Africa's Government and Religion

1. kings
2. trade
3. gold dust
4. sister
5. provinces
6. loyal
7. religions
8. spirits
9. Mansa Musa
10. Islam
11. mosques
12. Makkah
13. West Africa
14. Songhai
15. Timbuktu
16. 150
17. Quran
18. Swahili
19. Muslim
20. Europeans

13-3 African Society and Culture

1. The Bantu left their homeland and slowly inhabited all parts of Africa. Their traditions and language were spread all over the continent.
2. The family formed the basis of African society.
3. Storytelling helped teach children about their history and also gave them lessons about life, sometimes in the form of proverbs.
4. Two female African rulers were Queen Dahia al-Kahina and Queen Nzinga.

5. The Quran forbade any Muslim to enslave another Muslim, but non-Muslim slaves were allowed.

6. Europeans used enslaved Africans to do the hard labor of harvesting sugarcane, cotton, and grapes. They later used enslaved people in America to grow tobacco, rice, and cotton.

7. The African Diaspora is the spreading of African people and culture around the world.

8. Religion affected African art in the form of masks and statues, which Africans used to celebrate their beliefs.

9. Africans used dancing because they believed it allow the spirits to express themselves. They used it to celebrate important events including births and deaths.

10. African culture remains alive due to storytelling, art, and music.

Activity for Differentiated Instruction 14

1. Students' answers will vary. One possible answer: A samurai always fights back, even in impossible circumstances. It is better to die than to fail to fight.

2. The samurai did not admire scholarship or poetry writing. Students' answers regarding reasons the samurai rejected these virtues will vary. One possible answer: The samurai were men of action, and intellectual study did not seem especially useful or strong.

Critical Thinking Activity 14

1. Students' answers may vary, but should include specifics about the different clans such as where each was located and the size of their territory. For example, the Taira were located in Southern Japan and had a large territory.

2. The territory controlled by the Fujiwara expanded northward in A.D. 600, A.D. 800, and A.D. 1000.

3. In summarizing Japan's political state, answers may vary but could include the idea that Japan was not ruled by any one person in 1183, but many clans, and probably in a near-constant state of war, because of all the different clans and the territories they held.

4. Student answers will vary but should reflect an awareness that the sea is a natural barrier to expansion.

5. Students' answers may vary, but could include the idea that the Minamota Yoshinaka clan potentially had the strongest power base because it was centrally located in Japan, and had the larger cities of Kyoto and Nara located in it.

Geography and History Activity 14

1. Another volcano is believed to have erupted over the old one, giving the mountain its perfect cone shape.

2. "fire" or "deity of fire"

3. It is believed that Asama resides in the volcano. She is believed to have the power to make the flowers bloom and the crops grow. For many years, women were forbidden to climb Mount Fuji.

4. Shinto and Buddhism

5. Shikoku

6. Answers will vary, but students may suggest that ancient people did not have the scientific technology of today, and legends were developed to explain the behavior of something they did not understand.

People to Meet Activity 14

1. A mendicant is a homeless monk.

2. Shingon Buddhists focus their meditations by using mudra (prayer movements), mantra (sacred words), and mandalas (pictures representing the universe).

3. Answers will vary.

Time Line Activity 14

1192 Minamoto Yoritomo becomes the first shogun

1274 Mongols try to invade Japan

1331 The emperor rebels against the Kamakura shogunate

1333 Ashikaga Takauji makes himself shogun

1467 The Onin War begins

1567 The Ashikaga shogunate ends

1603 Tokugawa Ieyasu founds a shogunate

1867 The last shogun resigns

Citizenship and Service Learning Activity 14

Student answers to the Questions to Consider will vary. These questions require students to use examples from their daily lives and to think critically about issues that affect them. Students should answer the questions by using complete sentences and by supporting their opinions with logical arguments. Students should complete the Citizenship and Service Learning Activity Task by working individually or in a group as directed in the How to Do It section. At the end of the project, have students review their work by discussing any difficulties they faced while they completed the project and how they resolved those difficulties. Encourage students to explain how they would improve their work if they did this project again.

Economic Activity 14

1. ($12,000 – $7,150 = $4,850; $4,850 × 0.15 = $727.50; $727.50 + $715 = **$1,442.50**)

2. ($32,000 – $29,050 = $2,950; $2,950 × 0.25 = $737.50; $737.50 + $4,000 = **$4,737.50**)

3. ($120,000 – $70,350 = $49,650; $49,650 × 0.28 = $13,902; $13,902 + $14,325 = **$28,227**)

4. ($6,000 × 0.10 = **$600**)

5. ($75,000 – $70,350 = $4,650; $4,650 × 0.28 = $1,302; $1,302 + $14,325 = **$15,627**)

6. ($330,000 – $319,100 = $11,000; $11,000 × 0.35 = $3,850; $3,850 + $92,592.50 = **$96,442.50**)

World Literature Reading 14

1. Shikibu's husband and the Empress Dowager have both died.

2. Her husband's daughter sent cherry blossoms.

3. She was sad and distracted. She asks, "Is the child then led astray" by her father's writing?

4. because the dead blossoms beneath the trees would be reminders of how beautiful they were when they were alive

5. Shikibu used many words that showed her sadness, like "dark, dyed black." She also wrote about crying and about grieving the falling of the flowers.

Primary Source Reading 14

1. Priests, monks, soothsayers, ladies of the courts, substitutes, abbots, and dignitaries surrounded the queen.

2. The people around the queen were praying and reading sutras; telling the future; misleading evil spirits.

3. Eight million gods were listening to the priests' prayers.

4. Students will probably note that the birth of a prince, a son, will ensure the continuation of the dynasty.

Take Home Review Activity 14

Standardized Test Practice

1. A

Activity 14

1. shogun
2. feudalism
3. tanka
4. shrine
5. animism
6. Shotoku
7. Kamakura
8. clan
9. Heian
10. sects

Password phrase

The Tale of Heike

Vocabulary Activities

Section 14-1 Early Japan: Words to Know

1. Jimmu
2. shrine
3. clan
4. animism
5. Jomon
6. constitution
7. Shotoku
8. isolation
9. isolated

Section 14-2 Shoguns and Samurai: Words to Know

1. False; samurai
2. False; shogun
3. True.
4. False; Ashikaga Takauji
5. False; vassal
6. True.
7. False; Minamoto Yoritomo
8. principal
9. principal
10. principle

Answer Key

Section 14-3 Life in Medieval Japan: Words to Know

1. martial arts
2. meditation
3. calligraphy
4. tanka
5. guilds
6. SECT: a smaller religious group that is a division of a larger group
7. Answers will vary. A sample response would be: The design of a Japanese garden was special. The plantings and features of the garden made people who entered the area feel relaxed.

Guided Reading Activities

14-1 Early Japan

- **I.** islands
  - **A.** mountains
  - **B.** 20, seafood
- **II.** Jomon, knotted clay
- **III.** Yayoi
  - **A.** farming, paddies
  - **B.** potter's wheel
  - **C.** bells
  - **D.** clans
- **IV.** Yamato, Akihito
- **V.** Shotoku, China
  - **A.** constitution
  - **B.** Buddhist
- **VI.** animism
  - **A.** shrines
  - **B.** Shinto

14-2 Shoguns and Samurai

1. False. During the Nara period, the city of Nara was Japan's capital and the center of government and religion.
2. False. Unlike China, Japan did not use examinations to hire government officials. Instead, it hired nobles from powerful families.
3. True.
4. True.
5. True.
6. False. Samurai were not supposed to care for wealth, and believed in courage, bravery, and honor.
7. False. The Gempei War was a civil war between Japan's two most powerful clans.
8. True.
9. False. The Mongols were defeated due to the violent Pacific storms that the Japanese named "kamikaze."
10. True.

14-3 Life in Medieval Japan

1. religion
2. Buddhism
3. Shinto
4. sects
5. Pure Land
6. Zen
7. martial arts
8. meditation
9. China
10. Korea
11. lacquer
12. origami

13. calligraphy

14. rice

15. markets

16. trade

17. Women

18. obey

19. marriages

Activity for Differentiated Instruction 15

1. Answers will vary. One possible answer: They were different because today's laws are more concerned with individual civil rights than the laws of medieval England. They were the same because, like today, they were intended to maintain order in society.

2. Answers will vary. One possible answer: Maud/Matilda Fitzwalter would probably not face imprisonment today for rejecting the romantic interest of the king.

Critical Thinking Activity 15

1. D

2. A

3. Student's answers may vary, but should state that homes built in London today would probably not be built the same way as they were in medieval London. The most obvious reason is that the risk of fire would be great, as the houses were built mostly of wood and had an open fireplace in the middle of a room.

Geography and History Activity 15

1. They liked the island's isolation.

2. Rather than leveling the top of the mountain, he had a foundation built against the side of the mountain to support the structure.

3. The tides and quicksand made assaults on the island dangerous.

4. four; The monks needed to grow their own food since they were isolated from the mainland.

5. Answers will vary but students should note that kings and dukes recognized the natural protection that the monastery offered.

People to Meet Activity 15

1. An abbess is the nun in charge of everyone and everything that is in a convent.

2. Hildegard wrote about art, medicine, natural history, and theology. She also wrote about her visions.

3. Answers will vary.

Time Line Activity 15

ASIA AND AFRICA

1347 The plague is carried to Alexandria, Egypt

1348 The plague moves to Libya and Damascus

1349 The plague reaches Makkah

1353 The plague erupts again in China

EUROPE

1346 The plague appears in Caffa

1347 The plague appears in Sicily

1348 The plague reaches Pisa

1349 The plague spreads through France and Germany

1351 The plague reaches Eastern Europe

Citizenship and Service Learning Activity 15

Student answers to the Questions to Consider will vary. These questions require students to use examples from their daily lives and to think critically about issues that affect them. Students should answer the questions by using complete sentences and by supporting their opinions with logical arguments. Students should complete the Citizenship and Service Learning Activity Task by working individually or in a group as directed in the How to Do It section. At the end of the project, have students review their work by discussing any difficulties they faced while they completed the project and how they resolved those difficulties. Encourage students to explain how they would improve their work if they did this project again.

Economic Activity 15

1.

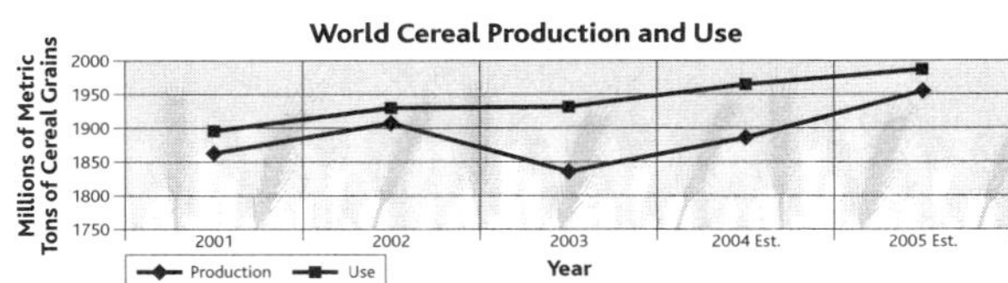

2. All years shown on graph (2001–2005)

3. Students should note that usage has been greater than production in each year. If this trend continues, supplies will run low, and there may not be enough grain for everyone.

4. Either the world production of grain must increase or demand for grain must decrease by slowing the growth in population.

World Literature Reading 15

1. He wanted to teach her that he was in charge of the family and that no matter how silly his commands were, she had to obey them.

2. First he told her to take the pot off the fire. Next he told her to put it behind the door. Last, he wanted her to put it on top of the hen-roost.

3. She poured the stew on his head and said that now the stew was where she wanted it.

4. The moral of the story is that a husband should not make unreasonable requests of his wife, because if he does, she may turn against him.

Primary Source Reading 15

1. Patience and not being disturbed by suffering bring true gladness.

2. When Saint Francis knocks at the gate, he is cold, covered in ice, and bloody.

3. A friar refuses to let Saint Francis in.

4. Student answers will vary. In general, they should reflect on the simplicity of his answer and the simplicity of his life. Great things do not bring happiness—only simple patience and peace can do that.

Answer Key

Take Home Review Activity 15

Standardized Test Practice

1. C

Activity 15

Moving from left to right on the time line, the order should be as follows:

A.D. 800	Feudalism begins in Europe
1050	Most people in Western Europe are Catholic
1095	Pope Urban calls the First Crusade
1100	Flanders and Italy exchange goods regularly
1200	Guilds are widespread in Europe
1215	King John is forced to sign the Magna Carta
1240	Mongols swept into the Kievan Rus
1346	The Black Death arrives in Europe

1. After. The First Crusade was called in 1095 and feudalism began in 800.
2. No. Feudalism began before guilds were widespread.
3. 1346
4. No. King John signed the Magna Carta in 1215, long after Flanders and Italy were exchanging goods in 1100.
5. 106 years (1346 – 1240 = 106)

Vocabulary Activities

Section 15-1 The Early Middle Ages: Words to Know

1. missionaries
2. Charlemagne
3. Clovis
4. excommunicate
5. Otto I
6. concordat
7. Gregory the Great
8. Charles Martel
9. fjords
10. enabled; C

Section 15-2 Feudalism: Words to Know

1. serf
2. fief
3. knight
4. guild
5. vassal
6. feudalism
7. C; Answers will vary. Student may write a sentence similar to this: No matter how big the portion of pie was, it was never big enough for him.

Section 15-3 Kingdoms and Crusades: Words to Know

1. False; grand jury
2. True.
3. False; Philip II

4. True.

5. False; William the Conqueror

6. False; trial jury

7. False; King John

8. A guarantee is a pledge or assurance that something agreed upon will take place.

9. A guarantee is stronger and more definite than a promise.

Section 15-4 The Church and Society: Words to Know

1. heresy

2. scholasticism

3. vernacular

4. theology

5. anti-Semitism

6. MASS: Catholic worship service

7. A summary is a brief statement covering the main points.

8. Answers will vary. Students may mention summaries they write for homework assignments or summaries they read, such as those at the end of a chapter.

Section 15-5 The Late Middle Ages: Words to Know

1. plague

2. plague

3. Joan of Arc

4. *Reconquista*

5. Isabella of Castile

6. Ferdinand of Aragon

7. something seen in a dream or trance

8. a mental picture or idea

Guided Reading Activities

15-1 The Early Middle Ages

1. The rivers of Europe were important because they made trade easier and provided safety from war.

2. The Celts were pushed aside by the Angles and Saxons and fled to the mountains.

3. The Franks became Catholic because their king named Clovis became Catholic, winning the support of the Romans living in the kingdom.

4. The Battle of Tours stopped the Muslim advance into Europe and helped Christianity remain Europe's major religion.

5. Charlemagne was declared by the pope to be the new Roman emperor.

6. Charlemagne was concerned because he did not want people to think that the pope had the power to decide who was emperor.

7. The Vikings came from Scandinavia.

8. Otto I was declared the Roman emperor because he sent troops to Italy to protect the pope as well as to defeat the Magyars.

9. Otto's territory was called the Holy Roman Empire.

10. Gregory the Great wanted monks to become missionaries because he wanted all of Europe to become Christian. Missionaries are people who are sent out to teach their religion.

11. Monasteries were schools, a place of rest to travelers, and hospitals.

12. The Concordat of Worms was an agreement between the pope and the king that stated only the pope could choose bishops and only the emperor could give the bishops jobs in government.

15-2 Feudalism

1. True.

2. False. The noble's castle or fortress was at the center of a feudal territory.

3. True.

4. False. The invention of the stirrup allowed knights to ride horses.

5. False. Serfs were not slaves, because they could not be sold and land could not be taken from them by the lord.

6. True.

7. False. The invention of the horse collar improved farming because horses could plow much faster than oxen.

8. True.

9. False. Only men could be citizens of a city, but only if they were born there or had lived there a certain amount of time.

10. True.

11. True.

15-3 Kingdoms and Crusades

1. William the Conqueror, a descendant of the Vikings, was the king of Normandy who conquered England.

2. William gave his knights land to keep them loyal.

3. William's officials and nobles spoke French.

4. Henry II set up courts of law to increase his power.

5. A grand jury determines if a person should be accused of a crime, and a trial jury determines if an accused person is guilty or innocent.

6. The Magna Carta was important because it limited the power of the government and recognized that people have rights.

7. Edward I introduced the Parliament, which made laws and advised the king.

8. Philip IV met with the clergy (priests), the nobles, the townspeople, and the peasants in his parliament.

9. Moscow was an important city because it was at the crossroads of several trade routes.

10. A crusade is a holy war.

11. The First Crusade drove the Muslims from the region, but the rest of the crusades achieved little.

12. The crusades increased trade between Europe and the Middle East, and they helped reduce feudalism.

15-4 The Church and Society

I. monasteries
- **A.** Cistercian
  - **1.** Bernard of Clairvaux
- **B.** convents
- **C.** Friars
- **D.** mass

II. Catholic
- **A.** Inquisition, heresy
- **B.** Jews

III. economy
  A. cathedrals
  B. universities, theology
    1. Thomas Aquinas
      a. natural law

15-5 The Late Middle Ages

1. plague
2. 38
3. feudal
4. Hundred Years'
5. French
6. English
7. Orléans
8. Joan of Arc
9. French
10. Muslims
11. Christians
12. *Reconquista*
13. Granada
14. Isabella of Castile
15. Ferdinand of Aragon
16. Spain
17. Catholic
18. Spanish Inquisition
19. Jews
20. Muslims